EARTH, MOON AND PLANETS

The Five Brightest Planets.

(Photographs by E. C. Slipher, Lowell Observatory.)

THE HARVARD BOOKS ON ASTRONOMY

Edited by

HARLOW SHAPLEY AND BART J. BOK

EARTH, MOON

AND

PLANETS

BY

FRED L. WHIPPLE

THE BLAKISTON COMPANY

Philadelphia

CONTENTS

PHOTOGRAPHS

Please note that in this book the photographic illustrations of celestial objects are intentionally inverted. The south direction is at the top and the north direction at the bottom. Since the astronomical telescope ordinarily inverts the image, the celestial objects are portrayed here with the same orientation that they present telescopically.

AUTHOR.

1

INTRODUCING THE PLANETS

THE FIVE BRIGHT PLANETS HAVE BEEN KNOWN TO MAN FOR many thousands of years, but in antiquity as mysterious celestial deities whose very motions seemed to reflect the caprices of superhuman beings. The old Greek and Roman legends are well known. Mars was the God of War, Venus the Goddess of Love, while Mercury was a sort of messenger boy. And thus the planets remain today—to the poets, that is, and to others for whom imagery is the essence of life. But to the scientist the planets have assumed a new character; the massive spheres of stone and iron and gas are even more interesting and exciting individually than were their mythical other-selves. Their motions are now a matter of mathematical calculation, not of caprice. The question of what lies within and beneath the cloud-filled atmosphere of Venus is, for the scientist, more conducive to mental activity than the folklore of dead generations.

Each planet acquires more individuality and becomes more interesting as the astronomer, by observation and reasoning, deduces additional facts. Every year some of the problems of the preceding year are solved and new ones, once beyond the expectation of solution, appear within

1

reach. To appreciate the current discoveries and deductions in planetary astronomy, we must be familiar with the fund of knowledge already accumulated.

To proceed towards an understanding of the solar family of planets, their dependents and the other inhabitants of this realm, an introduction is first in order. As everyone knows, the process of meeting a numerous family *en masse* may be both exhilarating and confusing. We shall proceed quickly with the introductions and then spend some time with each member of the family to develop more intimate acquaintanceships. *

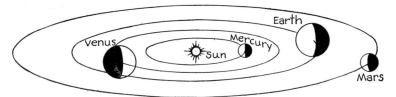

Fig. 1.—Orbits of the inner planets about the Sun.

A projection. The relative sizes of the planets are indicated. On the scale used, the Sun's diameter would be three feet.

The planets are really so small compared to the vast distances between them, and their reflected sunlight is so weak in comparison with the great brilliancy of the Sun, that all of them can never show to good advantage from any one location. As a vantage spot for observations, our present position on the Earth is actually quite satisfactory, except for the thick atmosphere above us. Since we must surmount this obstacle, we might as well, in imagination, go out farther from the Sun to about the distance of Jupiter. From there the inner part of the solar system is easily visible (Figure 1). The orbits of the planets as sketched in the figure show first

---

* Most of the numerical constants of distances, diameters, etc., are also given in Appendix III.

that the Sun is almost exactly in the center. The reason is very simple; the Sun possesses 99.866 per cent of the entire mass, so that by gravitational attraction it completely dominates the motions of the planets.

We notice next that the orbits lie almost in a plane, very close to the *ecliptic* or the plane of the Earth's orbit about the Sun. This favoritism on the part of the planets in adopting a common plane of motion is probably not due to chance. Although no rigorous proof has been given, it is possible that Jupiter is responsible, because this planet is 317 times as massive as the Earth and possesses seven tenths of the combined mass of all the planets. Jupiter is certainly the master planet and by gravitational attraction may have regulated the orbits of the others. There is the more likely possibility, of course, that the planets were all formed in a plane—but we must investigate this matter later on.

Mercury, * the smallest planet, moves in the smallest orbit of all, but one that is tipped from the common plane with an inclination of seven degrees, while the other inner planets keep within about three degrees of the plane.

For measuring distances in the solar system we must use a larger unit than for distances on the Earth. The most convenient is the astronomical unit (A.U.), which equals the mean of the greatest and least distances from the Earth to the Sun, technically called the Earth's mean distance. In miles it is 92,870,000, the zeros shouting that we do not know what numbers to put in for them, and that we are not very certain about even the number seven. This basic astronomical unit is very difficult to measure accurately in miles, and is known barely to one part in ten thousand.

The distance to the Sun is enormous in terms of ordinary distances on the Earth. An airplane, moving with the velo-

---

* One of its rare photographs is shown in the frontispiece. By E. C. Slipher, Lowell Observatory.

city of sound, 750 miles per hour, would require fourteen years for the trip (necessarily one-way), while a cannon projectile moving a mile per second would arrive in a little less than three years. If such distances seem large, remember that we spend our lives confined to one of the smaller planets of the solar system, and are denied the privilege of a

Fig. 2.—An asteroid moves through a field of stars.

Because of time exposures, an asteroid's motion produces a trailed image. (*Photograph by the Harvard Observatory.*)

"fuller" existence in the universe at large. The astronomical unit is actually much too small for conveniently listing the distances between the stars; a much larger unit is used for that purpose.

Mercury has a mean distance from the Sun of only 0.39 astronomical units, Venus 0.72, the Earth 1.00, Mars 1.52, and Jupiter 5.20, a rather uniform sequence* of increasing dis-

* See Appendix I for Bode's Law, a convenient memory scheme.

tances except for the large gap between Mars and Jupiter. In this gap we find more than a thousand* small planets called asteroids that fill the space where a planet might well move (see Figure 2 and note Figure 7, later). These asteroids range from mountain size, a mile or so in diameter, up to Ceres which is about 480 miles across—comparable to a large island. Pallas comes second with a diameter of 304 miles and Vesta third, 240 miles. There are certainly no large asteroids that have not been discovered but there must be many smaller ones, perhaps 40,000 that could be photographed with the larger telescopes. These fly-weight planets, although contributing a negligible part to the mass of the system (perhaps $\frac{1}{500}$ of the Earth's mass), provide astronomers with a great amount of work in observation and calculation. They are fine test specimens for theories of various kinds and may eventually assist materially in finding the key to the origin of the system.

Fig. 3.—The new Moon.
(*Photograph by the Lick Observatory.*)

The planets themselves have much of the character of the ancient gods for whom they were named. Mercury is

* By 1941 some 1500 were recognized.

indeed swift and small, characteristic of a messenger. It requires only 88 days for a complete revolution about the Sun, less than one fourth the length of our year. Its diameter is only 0.4 that of the Earth. Even this small diameter, 3100 miles, is enough greater than the diameter of Ceres to distinguish Mercury definitely as a planet rather than as a large asteroid. The period of rotation remains quite uncertain at present but probably equals the period of revolution

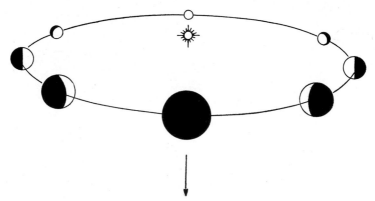

Fig. 4.—The phases of Venus relative to the Earth.

The synodic period of the phases is completed in 584 days. See Figure 5 for corresponding photographs.

about the Sun. The planet is, unfortunately, so small and always remains so close to the Sun as observed from the Earth, that surface markings are difficult to discern.

Venus is certainly the "sister" planet of the Earth. The diameter is almost identical (97.3 per cent), the period of revolution about the Sun somewhat shorter (225 days), and the mass about 0.8. Venus too is cloaked with a large atmosphere; it is this opaque atmosphere that hides the surface features so completely that we cannot be certain of the rate of rotation. From indirect evidence we judge the period probably to be long (Chapter 12)—more than three weeks. The actual observations of both of these inner planets are made difficult by the circumstance that we can see only part

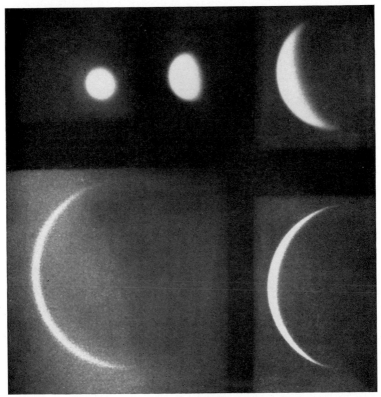

Fig. 5.—Venus.

Photographs with a constant magnification, at various phases. (*Photographs by E. C. Slipher, Lowell Observatory.*)

of the sunlit face at any time. When nearest to the Earth, only a thin crescent of Venus can be seen, as is the case for the Moon when new (see Figure 3), because the bodies are almost on a line between the Earth and the Sun. Figure 4 shows the various positions of Venus when the photographs of Figure 5 were made.*

Mars may best be described as a pygmy Earth (one half its diameter) with a thin atmosphere, distinct surface features (Frontispiece), but no oceans. It moves more slowly about the Sun, in 687 days. Mars, however, boasts two moons or satellites, while Mercury and Venus have none. These two satellites are little more than medals for Mars,

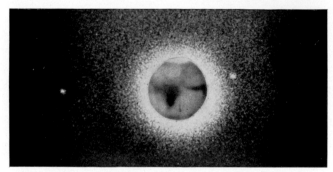

Fig. 6.—Mars, Deimos and Phobos.

Deimos is at the left, Phobos to the right of Mars' disc. The planetary image was overexposed in photographing the faint satellites, and was replaced by a normally exposed image. (*Photograph by E. C. Slipher, Lowell Observatory.*)

the God of War, since the largest, Phobos, is only fifteen miles across. Deimos, the smaller, is just one half of Phobos in diameter. The existence of these Lilliputian satellites, strangely enough, was narrated by Jonathan Swift in his "Gulliver's Travels," some one hundred and fifty years before their discovery in 1877. According to Gulliver's account, the astronomers of the cloud island, Laputa, possessed small but most excellent telescopes and had "discovered two lesser stars, or satellites, which revolve about Mars; whereof the innermost is distant from the center of the

---

* For the names of the various planetary configurations, see Appendix II.

Fig. 7.—Orbits of the outer planets about the Sun.

A projection. Pluto passes within Neptune's orbit, but does not intersect it because of the inclination. Note the asteroids and the relatively small size of Mars' orbit.

primary planet exactly three of his diameters, and the outermost, five; the former revolves in the space of ten hours, and the latter in twenty-one and a half." *

These periods of revolution are remarkably close to the truth, for Phobos revolves about Mars in 7 h. 39 m. while Deimos requires 30 h. 18 m. The mythical distances from the center of Mars, are, however, too great; Phobos is distant only 1.4 of the planet's diameter, and Deimos 3.5 diameters (see Figure 6). It would be enlightening to have learned more of the Laputian discoveries, but Gulliver mentions only that they had "observed ninety-three different comets, and settled their periods with great exactness."

The rapid motion of Phobos makes this satellite unique in the solar system. Its period of revolution is less than the Martian day, 24 h. 37 m. As seen from the surface of Mars, Phobos would rise in the west and set in the east!

Before going on to the outermost planets, we note that the four planets Mercury, Venus, Earth, and Mars are really very much alike, of somewhat the same size, and all fairly dense, as though they were made of stone or iron. They are justly classed as the *terrestrial* planets because of their

* Laputa, Chapter 3.

Fig. 8.—Jupiter.

Photographs made at different times with the 100-inch reflector at the Mount Wilson Observatory. The satellite Ganymede appears at the edge of the disc and its shadow on the disc of the upper right image. (*Photographs by the Mount Wilson Observatory.*)

similarity to the Earth. Probably Pluto is much like the Earth or Venus. Jupiter, Saturn, Uranus and Neptune, on the other hand, are of an entirely different species, giants compared to the Earth, and only about as dense as water. Their orbits are shown in Figure 7 as seen from beyond the distance of Pluto. On this small-scale chart the orbits of Figure 1 are all crowded into a small region about the Sun.

Jupiter is conspicuous as the greatest of the planets. It has eleven times the diameter of the Earth, but rotates faster than any other planet, its day being slightly less than ten hours in length. It rotates so fast, indeed, that the equator is much bulged out by the centrifugal force. Since Jupiter is only a third denser than water we are not surprised to find that it possesses an enormously thick atmosphere, how thick we cannot know. The depth of the atmosphere, if indeed there is a distinct solid surface below, can be calculated only on the basis of estimates of the chemical composition and temperatures within the planet. Ammonia

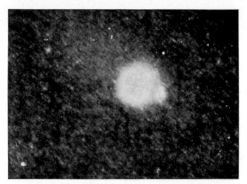

Fig. 9.—Neptune and its satellite.

and methane (marsh gas) are known to be present in the gigantic clouds that we can see from outside (see Figure 8). These markings are certainly clouds because their forms are ever changing. The general structure is banded parallel to the equator as though clouds were being blown along by "trade winds" that result from the rapid rotation.

The atmospheres of the other giant planets are very similar to that of Jupiter, the differences being attributable in a large measure to the fact that the planets farther from the Sun are colder at their surfaces. Neptune, 30 A.U. from the Sun, is a frigid world by our standards because it receives only $\frac{1}{900}$ as much heat and light from the Sun as we receive. Solid carbon dioxide (dry ice) near its melting point is hot compared to the probable temperature at the surface of Neptune, about −330°F. Nitrogen gas would be frozen, likewise oxygen.

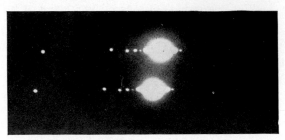

Fig. 10.—Six of Saturn's moons.

From left to right they are Titan, Rhea, Dione, Tethys, Mimas and Enceladus. The rings are "burned out" by the long exposures. (*Photographs by E. C. Slipher, Lowell Observatory.*)

Although the giant planets are cold and uninhabitable, their great masses and wide separation in space allow them

Fig. 11.—Saturn, the ringed planet.

(*Photograph by the Mount Wilson Observatory.*)

to control astonishingly large families of satellites. Jupiter is again first, with eleven moons, Saturn is second with nine, while Uranus has four and Neptune only one (see Figures 9 and 10). Of these, the four brightest of Jupiter's family, one of Saturn's, and the single satellite of Neptune are about the size of our Moon, while the others range in diameter from that of small asteroids to about half the Moon. The systems of Jupiter and Saturn are really miniature solar systems in every respect except that the primary planets do

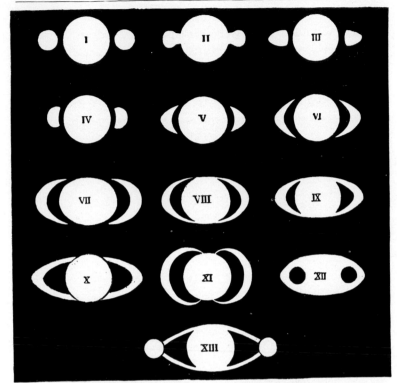

Fig. 12.—Early drawings of Saturn.
(*From "Splendour of the Heavens." Courtesy Hutchinson and Co.*)

not send out light by themselves but shine by reflected sunlight only. The great planets are more massive when compared to their largest satellites than is the Sun when compared to Jupiter or Saturn.

The similarity with the whole solar system is even more striking in the system of Saturn because this planet controls not only nine satellites, equal to the number of known planets about the Sun, but also possesses a family of miniature asteroids, which comprise the great rings (see Figures 10 and 11). These rings are so close to Saturn itself that in the early telescopes they looked like ears or appendages. Galileo, who was the first scientist of the modern world to see Jupiter's four bright satellites, sometimes drew Saturn as consisting of three pieces—a central body with symmetrical side sections (see Figure 12). We know now that the rings are made of small fragments of matter revolving about

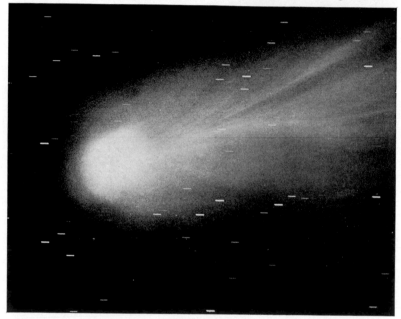

Fig. 13.—Head of Halley's comet.

During the nine-minute exposure the telescope followed the comet's motion on the star background. Therefore the star images are trailed. (*Photograph by the Mount Wilson Observatory.*)

Saturn in nearly a plane, relatively thinner than a sheet of paper. When seen at different angles they present different appearances, from invisibility, if seen edge on, to wide rings at the brightest angle possible.

On beyond Neptune lies the more recently discovered Pluto. Little is known about Pluto as a planet. Our best information suggests that it is slightly smaller and less massive than the Earth, but its rate of rotation is uncertain. Probably there is no atmosphere because the surface seems to reflect sunlight very poorly; the planets with heavy atmospheres reflect much better than those with thin

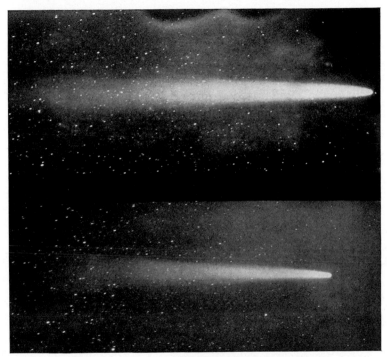

Fig. 14.—Two photographs of Halley's comet.
(*Photographs by the Mount Wilson Observatory.*)

atmospheres. The Moon is an especially poor reflector, and Pluto may be even worse.

To complete this quick introduction to the solar family, some mention must be made of the ever-baffling comets (Figure 13). These strange wanderers have excited more superstitious fear in the human mind than any other class of celestial bodies. Today their continued existence is in itself a major riddle of the solar system and the phenomena that they manifest are far from well explained. Most comets move in exceedingly elongated orbits, approaching the Sun for only a very small fraction of one period of revolution. When distant from the Sun they become too faint for observation but they brighten enormously at perihelion, when closest to the Sun. At this time they become so active that they waste an appreciable part of their substance into space, and produce a great coma of gases and small dust particles about their nuclei (see Figure 13). The strong sunlight forces these gases and dust back from the comet in a great tail, sometimes multiple and always complicated in structure. The structure and brilliancy of the tails are obvious from inspection of Figure 14.*

In later chapters we will become much better acquainted with each of the members of the solar family met in the present chapter. Each has a character more appreciated on closer contact. Also there are many provocative problems of structure and origin and even some family skeletons. In the next chapter we shall look into the important problem of family unity, the binding force that keeps each member in its place.

---

* For a complete discussion of comets, asteroids and small bodies in the solar system see "Between the Planets" by Fletcher G. Watson, Harvard Books on Astronomy.

2

HOW THE SYSTEM HOLDS TOGETHER

A MIGHTY AND ALL-PERVADING FORCE ENABLES THE SUN to hold the planets in their orbits of revolution, and empowers the planets to retain their satellites. The discovery of the universal law of gravitation, which describes this force, stands as a monumental feat of the human mind. Only a genius like Sir Isaac Newton could have started with the observational material and theories of his day, developed a new form of mathematics to solve the dynamical problems, and finally welded the observations and mathematical theory to form a simple yet universal law. A better understanding of his achievement can be obtained by glancing backward at the scientific foundation from which he started.

During the two centuries preceding Newton's activities, the best minds of European science had been amassing evidence and arguments to disprove the time-honored concept that the universe is centered on the Earth, which is benevolently lighted by the Sun, and has the Moon, planets and stars as cheerful decoration. Nicholas Copernicus* is

---

* Born on the border of Poland and Germany, 1473 A.D.

credited with the major efforts in bringing into disrepute the idea of a fixed Earth, an idea long cherished by the followers of Aristotle, the ancient Greek philosopher. An early impression of planetary motions as seen from a fixed Earth is shown in Figure 15.

Once the concept of a moving Earth was recognized as possible, although not well proven, the subsequent task of finding out how the Earth moves and why it moves was still

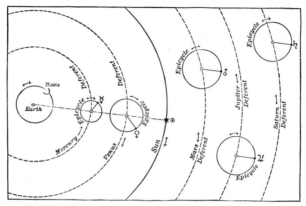

Fig. 15.—Ancient concept.

Planetary motions about a fixed Earth. According to the ancient Greco-Egyptian astronomer Ptolemy, the planets moved in small circles about "fictitious planets" that moved in large circles about the Earth. (*From Young's "General Astronomy." Courtesy Ginn and Co.*)

difficult. The stars, actually distant suns, are too far away to indicate by their yearly motion the 92,870,000 mile swing of the Earth about the Sun, even by the measures made for a long period after the invention of the telescope. One can very well sympathize with the critics of the new theory who stoutly maintained that solid earth was solid earth, obviously fixed in space. "If it were moving, as those young upstarts would have one believe, why do not the stars swing back and forth across the sky during the year?" The argument was absolutely sound, and has been disproved only during the last century by means of the most accurate observing techniques. The nearest star, α Centauri, is 270,000 astronomical units distant. From it the Earth's orbit would appear to have a radius smaller than the diam-

Fig. 16.—The Earth turns on its axis.

An eight-hour exposure with a fixed camera pointing at the north pole. Polaris produced the heavy trail near the center. (*Photograph by Fred Chappell, Lick Observatory.*)

eter of a human hair as seen fifteen yards away from the eye. Thus the yearly oscillation of α Centauri is an angle less than the apparent motion of the hair if moved through twice its diameter. For all other stars the annual motion is even smaller.

While the argument was raging about the motion of the Earth, the difficulty of predicting future positions for the Sun and planets, within the increasing degree of accuracy to which they could be observed, was becoming more and more serious. The invention of the clock accentuated the need for better predictions and more effective instruments to measure directions on the sky. It was necessary to know accurately how the planets actually moved through space. The daily rotation of the Earth (see Figure 16) and its yearly revolution, as we know today, complicate the problem enormously, because the observations must all be

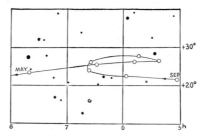

Fig. 17.—Mars followed this path

against the background of stars for four months. The circles represent positions at half-month intervals.

made from the Earth, a body itself in motion. In addition, light rays must pass through the atmosphere which can bend them as much as half a degree when near the horizon.

The effects of rotation and atmosphere can largely be removed if one establishes the relative positions of the stars in a fixed system covering the entire sky and then measures the positions of the planets with respect to the stars. The apparent motion of Mars during one opposition from the Sun is shown in Figure 17. This peculiar curve on the star background little resembles the smooth curve of the actual space motion already shown in Figure 1.

In the sixteenth century the great Danish astronomer, Tycho Brahe, set about doing what he could to improve the knowledge of planetary motions. His principle of action is one that should always be remembered by every scientist, because it embodies the very essence of good science. Tycho Brahe made quantities of the best observations possible with the best instruments he could obtain, then carefully studied his instruments to determine the size of the errors that should be expected. His long series of observations of Mars were minutely analyzed by John Kepler of Württemberg, who experimented with every kind of motion that he could devise for the planet. Some types of eccentric motions of Mars about the Sun would fit the observations *almost* as well as they should, but Kepler was obsessed by scientific ideals. His perseverance led him finally to discover three very simple laws describing the motion of a planet about the Sun. A simple law, if it fits the observations well, is almost always the true one in science. Kepler was certain that he had learned the truth about planetary motions, and time has corroborated his opinion.

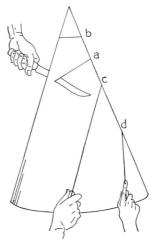

Fig. 18.—A cone is sectioned by a plane to produce (*a*) an ellipse, (*b*) a circle, (*c*) a parabola or (*d*) a hyperbola. These plane curves are called conic sections.

Kepler's first law states that *the orbit of a planet is an ellipse with the Sun at one focus.* Now an ellipse is one of the simplest closed curves on a plane, one that has always delighted mathematicians because of the many simple theorems to which it is susceptible. To obtain an ellipse is nearly as easy as to draw a circle. Simply take a cone (right-circular, if a mathematician is nearby) and slice it with a plane. The curve where the two intersect is an ellipse, as in (*a*) Figure 18.

You may, of course, be ingenious and pass the plane through the vertex to obtain only a point, or perpendicular to the axis to obtain a circle, (*b*), or parallel to a side. In the last mentioned case the ellipse never closes, becoming a parabola (*c*), or even a hyperbola (*d*), if the plane is more nearly vertical. These possibilities are no problem to the mathematician who calls all the possible curves *conic*

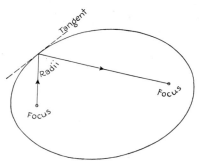

Fig. 19.—An ellipse.

Radii from the two foci make equal angles with a tangent. The eccentricity of this ellipse is 0.72.

sections and then proceeds to derive even more general theorems about them.

To identify the focus of an ellipse is only slightly more complicated than to slice the ellipse from a cone. If we draw a line from one focus and reflect the line from the ellipse at equal angles to the tangent, the line will always pass through the second focus, as in Figure 19. The situation is even simpler for a parabola where rays from the focus are reflected as a parallel bundle. This is the principle of a searchlight or an automobile headlight. In reverse, it is the principle of the reflecting telescope where parallel light rays from a distant star are brought to a point focus by reflection from the surface of a parabolic mirror (Figure 20).

Another noteworthy property of an ellipse is that from any point of the ellipse, the sum of the distances to the two foci is constant. This property suggests a very easy method of drawing. Stick two strong pins into a sheet of paper at the points where the foci are to be. Then place a closed loop of string about the two pins; stretch the loop taut with the point of a pencil, and draw the ellipse by swinging the pencil around the pins inside the taut loop (Figure 21). If the two pins are together one draws a circle, the simplest ellipse.

According to Kepler's first law, the Sun is always at one focus of the ellipse, the other focus being empty —a completely neglected mathematical point. Various possible orbits are drawn in Figure 22. The point nearest to the Sun is *perihelion* and the point farthest away is *aphelion*. The *mean distance* is half the sum of the perihelion and aphelion distances, or the semi-major axis of the ellipse. The shape of the orbit is measured by the *eccentricity*, which is the difference of the aphelion and perihelion distances divided by their sum. The eccentricity is zero for a circle, 1.0 for a parabola, and about 0.5 for a man's hat.

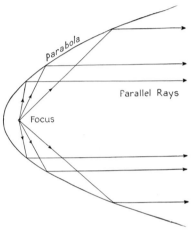

Fig. 20.—A parabola.

All radii from the focus are reflected into parallelism by a parabola.

The Earth's orbit is almost a circle with an eccentricity of only $\frac{1}{60}$. To the eye such an ellipse resembles a circle fairly well drawn, but the focus is clearly not in the center. Mercury and Pluto are the only planets with orbits that deviate much from circles, their eccentricities being 0.21 and 0.25, respectively. The distance of Pluto from the Sun thus varies from 30 A.U. at perihelion, just less than Neptune's mean distance, up to 50 A.U. at aphelion. One checks this calculation by noting that the mean of 30 and 50 is 40, the mean distance of Pluto in A.U., and noting that $(50 - 30)$ divided by $(50 + 30)$ is $^{20}\!/_{80}$ or 0.25, the eccentricity.

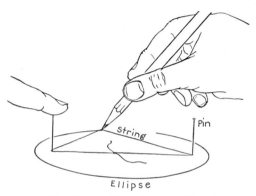

Fig. 21.—Drawing an ellipse

by means of two pins and a loop of string. This method works well except for the knot.

Kepler's second law of planetary motions is simpler than the first. It states that *a line joining a planet to the Sun sweeps out equal areas in equal intervals of time.* Accordingly, when a planet is near the Sun at perihelion it must move at a greater speed than when it is farther away, say at aphelion, as is shown in Figure 23. For Pluto the speed is 3.8 mi./sec. at perihelion and 2.3 mi./sec. at aphelion. The ratio is 5/3 as we might have guessed from the ratio of the two distances. At perihelion (about January 1), the Earth has increased its speed by 0.6 mi./sec. from its aphelion speed of 18.2 mi./sec.

Kepler's third law, the Harmonic Law, states that *the squares of the periods of revolution of the planets about the Sun are in the same ratio as the cubes of their mean distances.* This harmonic law provides an easy method for calculating the period if one knows the mean distance of a body revolving

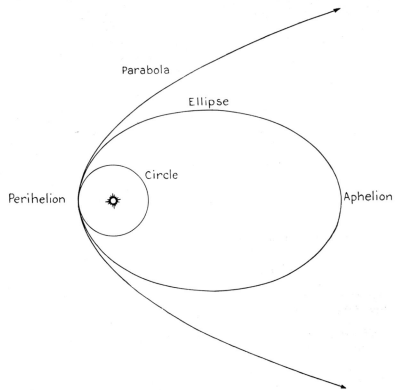

Fig. 22.—Various orbits about the Sun.

Comets follow orbits that are very elongated ellipses, nearly parabolic close to the Sun. Planetary orbits are ellipses.

about the Sun. Express the mean distance in astronomical units. Cube this distance. The square root of the cube is the period of revolution in years. For the Earth the formula checks; the square root of 1^3 is 1; the period of the Earth is 1 year. For Neptune the mean distance is 30 A.U. $30^3 =$

27,000. The square root of 27,000 is 164, Neptune's period in years. More accurately the period is 164.8 years, obtained by using a more precise value of the mean distance.

By means of Kepler's three laws, the Elliptic Law, the Law of Areas, and the Harmonic Law, a planet's motion can be predicted far into the future. Only two corrections are applied today. The first correction arises from the fact that one planet will disturb the motion of another; a second very slight correction must be made in the case of Mercury's orbit because of an effect predicted by Einstein's theory of relativity.

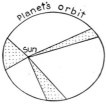

Fig. 23.—Equal areas are swept out in equal intervals of time. A planet moving in this orbit would pass through each of the shaded areas in the same time. Eccentricity of the ellipse is 0.5.

Newton was fully conversant with Kepler's laws for describing the motions of the planets and also with Galileo's* revolutionary idea that all bodies fall at the same rate regardless of size. Galileo had demonstrated this idea by dropping large and small cannon balls from the Leaning Tower of Pisa but had brought conviction to almost no one—except to himself for treason, religious treason in questioning tradition. Galileo held other equally scurrilous ideas, in particular that a moving body stopped moving only because its motion was impeded by friction, not because space had some intrinsic property that tended to stop all moving bodies.

Newton extended Galileo's ideas about the motion of material bodies in empty space and crystallized them into three simple laws. These principles of motion are so familiar to us today that they are listed only for the sake of completeness. The first states that *a body remains at rest or maintains a uniform motion in a straight line unless acted upon by a force;*

---

* Galileo Galilei, born at Pisa, Italy, in 1564 A.D.

the second states that *the rate of change of motion is proportional to the force acting;* and the third states that *action and reaction are equal but opposite in direction.* Obvious applications exist everywhere, especially in our modern world of machines. Lack of recognition of frictional forces, both with the air and between moving parts in machinery is the one difficulty that prevented the laws from being discovered much sooner.

With all of these principles in mind, Newton began to ponder the problems of the motions of the Moon and the planets. Since, by gravitation, the Earth attracts an apple, or a cannon ball or a feather, all with a force proportional to the mass, why should it not attract the Moon? By all rights the Moon should move in a straight line unless it is acted upon by a force—but the Moon actually moves in a curved path about the Earth. Therefore, it must be continually falling towards the Earth, the rate of fall being measured by the deviation from motion in a straight line (Figure 24). Thus, the attraction of the Earth must produce a force on the Moon of the exact magnitude to cause the Moon to fall as it does. In other words, the Earth's attractive force must exactly counterbalance the centrifugal force of the Moon in its revolution about the Earth. Newton found that if the force of gravitation varied inversely as the square of the distance from the center of the Earth, it would be reduced to the proper value at the Moon's distance.*

From Kepler's laws, Newton was also able to prove mathematically that the planets are attracted towards the Sun by a similar force. Putting all the evidence together he came to the conclusion that *every particle of matter in the universe attracts every other particle by a force that varies directly as the product of their masses and inversely as the square of the distance*

---

* It is said that Newton withheld publication of the law of gravitation for several years because of the difficulty in proving that the Earth attracts as though all of its mass were concentrated at the center.

between them. This universal law of gravitation accounts for all the complicated motions in the solar system to the high degree of accuracy possible in astronomical measurement (about one part in a million). The only error is a forward motion of the perihelion of Mercury, by about $50''$ in a century, which is explained by a slight correction to Newton's law as predicted by Einstein's theory of relativity. An

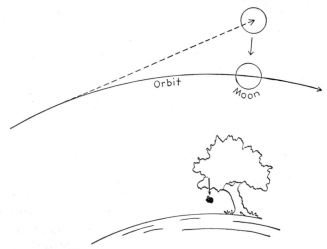

Fig. 24.—Falling Moon and apple.

Newton concluded that the Earth's gravity causes the Moon to fall from a straight-line motion and the apple to fall from a tree, according to the same law.

angle of $50''$ would be subtended by the iris of the eye at a distance of about fifty yards.

Thus the solar system holds together by the attraction of the Sun upon the planets, and the satellite systems by the attraction of the planets upon their satellites. The problem would be very simple and completely solved by Kepler's laws if it were not for the unhappy circumstance that all of the planets attract each other, as well as their satellites and the Sun. This universal attraction complicates the problem so much that there is no exact mathematical solution. The only saving grace lies in the fact that the planets are much less massive than the Sun so that the forces of interattraction, proportional to the masses, are much smaller than the attraction of the Sun. The satellites, likewise, are much less massive than their planets. Consequently, Kepler's laws can be used to obtain an approximate solution for the motions, small corrections being made on the basis of the interattractions. These corrections are known as *perturbations*, because the other planets perturb the motions of the one under investigation.

The most difficult problem of perturbations occurs in the Earth-Moon system where the Sun perturbs the motion of the Moon about the Earth. Strictly speaking, the Earth perturbs the motion of the Moon about the Sun because the Sun actually attracts the Moon with a force nearly twice as great as the attraction of the Earth on the Moon. Nevertheless, there is no danger that the Sun can steal the Moon away from the Earth and leave us without inspiration on warm summer nights. The system is so compact, the Earth and Moon moving so nearly together, that the Sun's attraction serves only to keep both bodies moving about it in an average path that is elliptic. The chief results are: first, that the Moon's orbit is never *convex* towards the Sun (Figure 25), and, second, that astronomers have much more work to do in predicting the Moon's motion. The single equation for the exact motion of the Moon covers some 250 large-size pages.

Among the planets, Jupiter is definitely the solar system's bad boy in disturbing the motions of all the planets and asteroids. With a mass equal to $\frac{1}{1000}$ that of the Sun, a "lion's share" of the mass of the entire planet family, Jupiter produces by far the largest perturbations, particularly among the asteroids which are nearest to it in space (Figure 7). If the orbit of an asteroid is calculated, and calculations made without allowing for Jupiter's attraction, the errors of prediction may amount to several degrees within a few years. Asteroids are sometimes "lost" in this fashion, until they are independently rediscovered and identified by their orbital path and brightness.

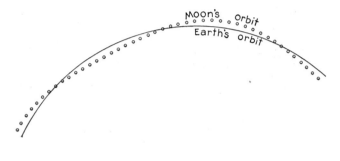

Fig. 25.—The Moon's orbit about the Sun.

The deviations from a perfect ellipse are greatly exaggerated in the diagram; even so, the Moon's orbit is always concave towards the Sun, as can be seen by tipping the page and sighting along the row of circles.

The asteroids also are forced to move with periods that are not related by simple fractions (e.g., $\frac{1}{2}$ or $\frac{1}{3}$) with the period of Jupiter. The reason is easy to see. Let us take the case that three revolutions of the asteroid require exactly the same time as two revolutions of Jupiter. Whatever perturbations are produced in three revolutions of the asteroid will be duplicated in the next three revolutions, and so on, eventually changing the orbit materially. The process is similar to that when an automobile passes over a series of equally spaced bumps in the road. If the speed is such that the natural period of vibration of the springs in the car equals the time between the bumps, the vibration is increased at each jolt until the springs break or until the driver

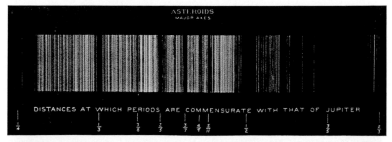

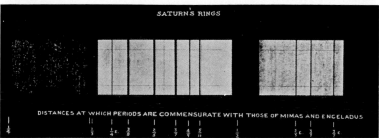

Fig. 26.—Kirkwood's gaps

in the mean distances of the asteroids (upper), and the gaps in the rings of Saturn (lower). Note the wide gaps at period ratios of $\frac{1}{2}$ and $\frac{1}{3}$. (*By Percival Lowell. From his biography by A. Lawrence Lowell. Courtesy the Macmillan Co.*)

changes the speed of the car. The asteroids are similarly forced to change their speeds when near the critical values. The result is that a curve of the numbers of asteroids plotted against the period shows conspicuous gaps* where the periods are commensurable with Jupiter's (see Figure 26).

---

* Known as the Kirkwood gaps, in recognition of their discoverer, an American astronomer of last century.

In Saturn's rings, which we have mentioned as similar to the asteroid system, exactly the same effect occurs. The fact that there are *rings* rather than a single ring is the result of the perturbations on the minuscule asteroids in the rings by three inner satellites, Mimas, Enceladus and Tethys. These satellites force the small particles in the rings to avoid certain speeds in moving about Saturn, with the result that dark spaces show at the critical distances. Cassini's division, the conspicuous dark space between the outer and middle rings in Figure 27, covers a region in which the tiny asteroids would move with periods of one half that of Mimas, one third that of Enceladus or one quarter that of Tethys, slightly more than eleven hours. Other expected "dark rings" can also be observed.

The fact, mentioned earlier, that there exists such a large ratio in mass between the Sun and the planets, and between the planets and their satellites, is not just a happy circumstance for the convenience of astronomers. It is exceedingly doubtful that the solar system could long exist were the planets comparable with the Sun in mass. No one of the bodies could stay near the center of gravity,* as the Sun does now in the solar system, but all would be moving in complex curves of almost unpredictable form. Although mathematics cannot give a useful solution even for the case of three bodies of nearly equal mass, it demonstrates that in our complicated case there would be disastrous results. Some planets would be eliminated by collisions and others by being tossed out of the system until, most probably, the system would eventually consist of two of the largest bodies moving about each other at a moderate distance, each with a smaller companion or a satellite system.

---

* The center of gravity is the point about which all the bodies would balance if supported by weightless rods under a uniform attraction similar to gravity on the Earth.

Fig. 27.—The complex rings of Saturn.

As drawn by Richard Proctor from visual observations. In the upper diagram the rings are nearly but not quite edge on. Their shadow is apparent on the disc. The five divisions can be seen only under the best conditions for observing. (*From* "*Old and New Astronomy.*" *Courtesy Longmans Green and Co.*)

A few other smaller bodies might remain in the system at very great distances from the largest ones. Our experience with double and multiple stars indicates that they tend to go in pairs separated by relatively large distances from other pairs in the system. Some astronomers are of the opinion that the asteroids may be the skeletal remains of a planet, possibly one that tried to compete with Jupiter.

At present there is no danger that the solar system will lose any planets or that any collisions of importance will occur. Our absolute certainty that there can be no disasters, however, covers only scores or hundreds of millions of years. The thought of possible disasters at a later period is really not very depressing at the moment.

3

THE DISCOVERIES OF NEPTUNE AND PLUTO

THE REMARKABLE STORY OF THE DISCOVERIES OF NEPTUNE and Pluto begins actually with the discovery of Uranus, because without observations of Uranus the two later discoveries would have been delayed for many years. Indeed, the detection of Uranus marks the beginning of a new epoch in the history of astronomy, for Uranus was the first planet to be "discovered." Mercury, Venus, Mars, Jupiter and Saturn have always been visible to the eye of any man who looked skyward (unless the eyes of our prehistoric ancestors were much inferior to our own).

Sir William Herschel, perhaps the most assiduous observer of all time, first detected the small disc* of Uranus in 1781. His account of the discovery shows clearly that he was not immediately certain of the true character of the new object. From the Philosophical Transactions of 1781 we read, "On Tuesday the 13th of March, between ten and eleven in the evening, while I was examining the small stars in the neighborhood of H Geminorum, I perceived one that appeared

---

* Three and three quarters seconds of arc.

35

visibly larger than the rest; being struck with its uncommon magnitude, I compared it to H Geminorum and the small star in the quartile between Auriga and Gemini, and finding it to be much larger than either of them, suspected it to be a comet."

Herschel's announcement of the new object as a comet

Fig. 28.—*Sir William Herschel*.

Three years after his discovery of Uranus. The title was conferred upon him later. (*From C. A. Lubbock's, "The Herschel Chronicle." Courtesy Cambridge University Press.*)

was natural and conservative, whatever he may have suspected concerning its true nature. Several months of observation and calculation were required to demonstrate that no cometary motion would satisfy the observations and that the "comet" could be nothing less than a new planet.

It was an extraordinary keenness of eye and judgment that enabled Herschel to distinguish the planet from the nearby stars, by its appearance alone. Other observers, while measuring the positions of neighboring stars, had seventeen times measured the position of Uranus and had noticed no unusual aspect. Some of the great contemporary astronomers had difficulty in identifying the planet even after they had been informed of its exact position on the sky.

Uranus did not become the planet's official name for several years. It first bore the title, "Georgium Sidus" (Herschel's appellation in honor of King George the Third) and was also called "Herschel" for its discoverer. The present name was finally adopted, in conformity with the naming of the other planets.

In spite of Uranus' slow motion (with a period of 84 years), its orbit could be well determined within a relatively short time after discovery because of the seventeen inadvertent observations made before Herschel noticed the disc. The first observation, made in 1690, was earlier by nearly a complete revolution of Uranus. The orbit calculators found some difficulty in reconciling all the observations but the chance for errors in the observations, or for deviations because of the perturbations by other planets, seemed great enough to account for the discrepancies. However, when Uranus began to deviate appreciably from its computed path, even after careful allowance had been made for the perturbations by Jupiter and Saturn, several astronomers began to suspect that an unknown planet might be disturbing the motion of Uranus.

In the second and third decades of the nineteenth century the deviations were large enough to arouse suspicion, but the mathematical difficulties in predicting the position of the unknown planet seemed insurmountable at that time. By the year 1845 Uranus had moved out of place by the "intolerable quantity" of two minutes of arc, an angle barely resolvable by the naked eye. Leverrier, the great French astronomer, showed in 1846 that no possible orbit for Uranus could reconcile all of the observations within their reasonable errors. He concluded that the deviations could be explained only by the hypothesis of an unknown massive planet beyond the orbit of Uranus.

Later in the year 1846 Leverrier completed his calculations for the position of the hypothetical planet, and was so confident of his analysis that he dared to predict its position and that it would show a recognizable disc. He sent his predictions to the German astronomer Galle, who discovered the actual planet *on the same night* that he received the prediction. Neptune's position on the sky lay within a degree, less than two Moon diameters, of the position forecast by Leverrier. Galle's immediate success was due to his access in Berlin to a new star chart of the sky region. A quick telescopic survey showed the new object where no star had been seen before. A close inspection verified the existence of a disc, too small to be distinguished easily.

Fig. 29.—Leverrier.

Whose prediction led to the discovery of Neptune. (*From Lebon, "Histoire de l'Astronomie." Courtesy McGraw-Hill Book Co.*)

Fig. 30.—Johann Galle.

Who discovered Neptune. (*From "Splendour of the Heavens." Courtesy Hutchinson and Co.*)

This remarkable discovery of a new planet by means of mathematical deduction is a landmark in the history of astronomy. Like many great discoveries, it must be credited to more than one man. While Leverrier had been making his brilliant calculations, a young and unknown English mathematician, J. C. Adams, arrived independently at the same result by a somewhat different method. Adams' calculations had, indeed, been completed some weeks before Leverrier's, but unlucky circumstances prevented the English observers from anticipating Galle's discovery. The Berlin star chart that had so materially assisted Galle was not then available in England. Hence the astronomer Challis, at Cambridge, began searching for the planet by the arduous method of plotting all the stars in the region, with the intent of re-observing them later in order to detect the planet by its motion. He was also busy observing comets, and did not study or compare his observations until after Galle's discovery. He then found, with chagrin, that on his fourth night of observing he could have identified Neptune, had he studied his observations! The expectation of a long and difficult task led him to wait until a mass of observations had accumulated, in order that the analysis might be more efficient—and so he missed his opportunity.

Fig. 31.—John Couch Adams.

Who also predicted Neptune's position. (*From "Splendour of the Heavens." Courtesy Hutchinson and Co.*)

Neptune might also have been found at the Royal Observatory in Greenwich, except for an inexplicable lethargy at that institution. The Astronomer Royal, it is true, was exceedingly busy, particularly with a practical problem for the government. He was in the midst of settling the question of the most expeditious railway gauge to be adopted as a standard. Therefore he did not center his attention on the planetary problem at hand.

The entire turn of events must have been heartbreaking for Adams, who had apparently planned his investigation some years before he had the opportunity to execute it. Posthumously the following note was found among his effects: "1841, July 3. Formed a design, in the beginning of this week, of investigating, as soon as possible after taking my degree, the irregularities in the motion of Uranus, which were as yet unaccounted for: in order to find whether they may be attributed to the action of an undiscovered planet beyond it, and if possible thence to determine the elements of its orbit, etc., approximately, which would probably lead to its discovery."

It is a pleasure to record that both Leverrier and Adams now share equally the honor of having predicted the existence and position of Neptune. Galle, of course, receives his full credit for actually having found it. Like Uranus, Neptune had been mistaken for a star in the course of previous measurements of stellar positions.

The conquest of the solar system by Newton's law of gravitation and by painstaking observation has been continued in the present century. Efforts have culminated in the discovery of Pluto, under circumstances surprisingly similar to those related for Neptune. Again, almost identical predictions were made by two men and again an early search actually included the new planet but perverse fortune prevented its detection until much later.

At the beginning of this century Percival Lowell, who founded an observatory at Flagstaff, Arizona for the purpose of observing the planets, particularly Mars, became actively interested in a possible trans Neptunian planet. He reinvestigated the orbit of Uranus and concluded that the apparent errors of observation could be materially reduced by the inclusion of perturbations by an unknown planet. His calculations of the orbit and positions of Planet X were not published until 1914, although his search for the planet was begun in 1905. Twenty-four years later, in 1929, a new thirteen-inch refracting telescope to expedite the search was completed, and was installed at the Lowell Observatory.

A young assistant, Clyde Tombaugh, was assigned the task of systematically photographing regions of the sky along the ecliptic. For each region he made two long-exposure photographs, separated in time by two or three days. Then, in search of the predicted planet, he very carefully compared the resulting photographic plates. Comparisons were made by means of a *blink microscope*, a double microscope apparatus which enables the observer to inspect the same area of the sky on two plates alternately. Any object that has moved on the sky during the interval between the two exposures appears to jump back and forth among the stars, which appear to remain fixed.

Within less than a year after the institution of its new observing program, the Lowell Observatory telegraphed the following announcement: "Systematic search begun years ago supplementing Lowell's investigations for Trans Neptunian planet has revealed object which since seven weeks has in rate of motion and path consistently conformed to Trans Neptunian body at approximate distance he assigned. Fifteenth magnitude. Position March twelve days three hours GMT was seven seconds West from Delta Geminorum, agreeing with Lowell's predicted longitude." (Sent March 12, 1930.)

The astronomical world soon unanimously adopted the name Pluto as appropriate to this planet, which moves in the outer regions of darkness. The first two letters of the name are, moreover, the initials of Percival Lowell, who had died in 1916, only two years after the publication of his detailed prediction. The symbol ♇ for Pluto, independently suggested by several people, was immediately accepted officially.

Lowell's prediction of the position of Pluto was not, however, the only one. William H. Pickering had also calculated positions for the new planet. In 1909 he published a prediction based on perturbations in the orbit of Uranus, and in 1919 published a revision which also included effects

Fig. 32.—Percival Lowell.

Whose prediction and enthusiasm led eventually to the discovery of Pluto. (*From Louise Leonard's "Percival Lowell." Courtesy Richard G. Badger Co.*)

arising in Neptune's orbit. He deduced that the unknown planet should have twice the Earth's mass and should be of magnitude 14.5*—almost precisely the observed value. Lowell's calculated value for the mass was seven times the Earth's, while the actual value is less than one (see Chapter IV). At the time of discovery the positions predicted by the two investigators were in almost perfect agreement, but in

---

* See Appendix IV for an explanation of the astronomical system of magnitude.

error by about 5 degrees along the plane of the Earth's orbit.

Subsequent orbits, based on prediscovery photographs of the new planet, show that it moves about the Sun with a period of 248 years,* in an orbit inclined 17 degrees to the mean plane of the other planets. At perihelion the orbit passes within that of Neptune, but because of the high inclination the two bodies can never collide.

Only the perversity of chance kept the discovery of Pluto from being made by the Mount Wilson astronomers in 1919. At that time, Milton Humason, at the request of Professor Pickering, photographed the regions around the predicted position and actually registered the planet on some of the plates. Pluto's image on one of the two best plates, however, fell directly upon a small flaw in the emulsion—at first glance it seemed to be a part of the flaw—while on the other plate the image was partly superimposed upon that of a star! Even in 1930, when the 1919 position was rather well known from the orbit, it was difficult to identify the images that had been produced by Pluto eleven years before.

It would appear ungenerous and rather futile to present the arguments which attempt to prove that the successful predictions by Lowell and Pickering were fortuitous. Their predictions led to Pluto's discovery. The relentless search for the planet, and its consequent discovery represent a crowning achievement in scientific progress. All of the members of the Lowell Observatory staff deserve the highest praise for the painstaking work and the consequent result.

A continuance of the Lowell Observatory search, covering the entire sky, indicates that there exist no more planets within the discovery range of the thirteen-inch telescope. If

---

*According to the orbit by S. B. Nicholson and N. U. Mayall.

other planets exist they must be considerable fainter than Pluto, which means that they must be either farther away, or smaller. To continue the quest for much fainter planets with one of the large telescopes, say the hundred-inch reflector at Mount Wilson, would be impractical. The larger telescopes progressively photograph smaller areas of the sky. A search of the entire sky to the limiting brightness easily attainable with the hundred-inch telescope would require its continuous use every hour of every clear moonless night for about a century. The discovery of possible planets beyond Pluto will be very difficult, unless luck plays a role or unless new observing techniques are developed.*

---

*The use of a large Schmidt-type camera (lens-mirror combination) shows promise in this field. See "Telescopes and Accessories" by George Z. Dimitroff and James G. Baker, Harvard Books on Astronomy.

4

WEIGHTS AND MEASURES

WEIGHING THE PLANETS AND FINDING THE DISTANCES between them are naturally most important in learning about their true character. Only from a knowledge of the masses can we begin to ascertain the real structure of the individual bodies. With the additional information concerning motions and distances we can make progress in retracing the history of the planetary system and in formulating predictions of its ultimate destiny.

THE DISTANCE TO THE SUN

By measuring the positions of the planets or asteroids and by applying Newton's law, astronomers can calculate planetary orbits about the Sun and predict future positions with high accuracy. The relative distances can be calculated with a precision equal to that of the most precise distances measured on the Earth, to about one part in a million. The surprising difficulty lies in the fact that these accurate distances are all in terms of the astronomical unit, the mean distance from the Earth to the Sun, not in terms of feet or miles. For purposes of prediction this uncertainty makes almost no difference, but no scientist relishes the use of a measuring rod with an unknown length.

In measuring the astronomical unit we are faced with the fact that the largest available measuring unit is the Earth itself; its dimensions are now known rather accurately. But the radius of the Earth is less than 1/20,000 of the astronomical unit; from the Sun it subtends an angle of only 8.80 seconds of arc, the geocentric parallax* of the Sun (see Figure 33). Although the Sun's parallax can be measured by simultaneous observations at two widely separated stations, the angle is so small that the percentage error becomes large; hence no precise determination of the length of the

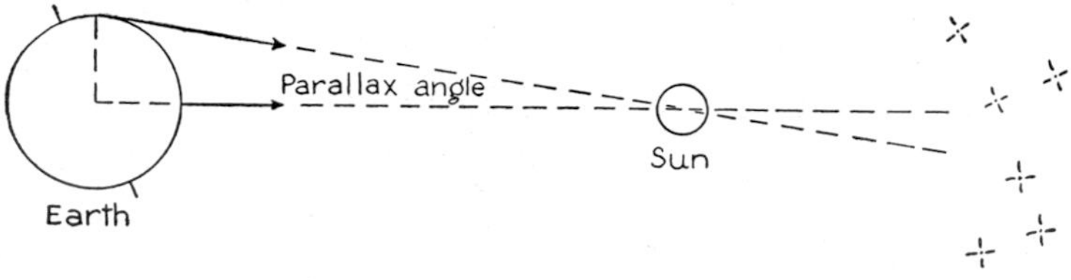

Fig. 33.—The Solar parallax
is the angle of the Earth's radius as seen from the Sun. The geocentric parallax of any celestial object is the corresponding angle from the object. See Figure 48 for stellar parallax.

astronomical unit can be made by measurements of the Sun's position.

A better method is to measure in miles the distance to some body that comes close to the Earth. Since the body's distance in astronomical units is given by an accurate orbit, we can compare the two values to find the number of miles in an astronomical unit. The Moon will not serve for precisely this purpose because its distance cannot be cal-

---

* The geocentric parallax of any object is the angle subtended by the Earth's radius perpendicular to the line of sight, as seen from the object. Parallax is inversely proportional to distance. The geocentric parallax must not be confused with the stellar parallax, for which the base line is one astronomical unit.

culated in astronomical units without introducing the Earth's mass. Mars, under the most favorable conditions, comes within only 34,600,000 miles of the Earth. Venus comes closer, 26,000,000 miles, but at that time it is nearly in the direction of the Sun and cannot be well measured (refer to Figure 4). The best object for the purpose turns out to be an asteroid, Eros.

It is a real pleasure to find a use for an asteroid because asteroids are generally more of a nuisance than a help in astronomy. When Eros comes within 14,000,000 miles of the

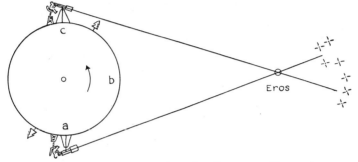

Fig. 34.—Measuring the distance to Eros.

The observer simply allows the Earth to move him from *a* to *c* in order that he may measure the parallax angle at Eros.

Earth, it gives a parallax of about seven times that of the Sun, or over a minute of arc. Furthermore, the asteroid looks and photographs like a star or a point of light; the resultant measurements are easy and very accurate. Observers, instead of choosing different parts of the Earth for their observations, can work independently. Each simply waits for the Earth to turn, and photographs the asteroid in the evening, at midnight and in the morning, as shown in Figure 34. The position of Eros among the stars changes because of the difference in the position of the observer with respect to the Earth. Knowing the instant of each photographic exposure and his exact position on the Earth, the observer can calculate the distance to Eros in miles just as accurately as though simultaneous observations were made at different stations on the Earth. The process is similar to that of estimating a small distance with only one eye by turning ones head, or by moving it from side to side.

The motion of Eros across the sky between the observations necessitates a major correction. When this correction and other minor ones are applied, the distance can be well determined. In January of 1931, Eros made one of its very close approaches to the Earth at a minimum distance of 16,200,000 miles.

International cooperation of the world's leading observatories was essential for the best possible determination of the distance from the Earth to Eros. Before the asteroid's actual approach, many stars along the calculated path were reobserved, to provide more accurate reference points for Eros' apparent direction. Even the colors of the stars were measured, in order that allowance could be made for the slight prismatic effect of the Earth's atmosphere. Special lenses were devised and special cameras built for the purpose of obtaining the most useful photographs. After this elaborate preparation, many hundreds of photographs were made at several observatories located over the entire globe.

The preparation and execution of the observing programs, however, did not constitute the major part of the entire work necessary for the problem. Measurement and reduction of numerous plates, and resultant multifarious calculations and corrections, are even more arduous and time consuming. Preliminary results of this investigation, combined with older results by various other methods, give a value of $8''.803$ for the solar parallax. The astronomical unit becomes 92,870,000 miles with a probable error of some 10,000 miles. The error may at first appear large, but after all, it is an error of only a part in ten thousand, which is comparatively minute.

WEIGHING THE EARTH

The first step in weighing the planets is to weigh the Earth. Archimedes* said that if he had a place to stand he could move the Earth by levers. He could equally well have weighed it by observing how easily it moved when he pulled the levers. We are actually interested, not in the weight of the Earth, but in its *mass*. The weight of a body is only a measure of the Earth's attraction for it, while its mass represents the quantity of matter that it contains. One of Newton's great discoveries was that the mass and weight are proportional. If we go back to Newton's laws of motion we find that mass is the measure of the force necessary to change the motion of a body by a certain amount. It takes more force to start a ten ton truck than a baby carriage because of the difference in mass. In empty space, away from attracting masses, neither the truck nor the baby carriage would have any weight, but their masses would be unchanged.

We know just how much force the Earth exerts on a unit mass through gravitation. This force is the surface gravity, which holds us down and enables us to *weigh* things. Since gravity is proportional to the Earth's mass the only unknown is the constant of attraction between two masses, i.e., the constant of gravity.†

One method of finding this constant is by measuring the attraction of a mountain on a plumb line. As in Figure 35,

---

* Greek mathematician, B.C. 287?–212.

† Newton's law of gravitation states that two bodies of masses m_1 and m_2 separated by a distance r are attracted by a force $\dfrac{Gm_1m_2}{r^2}$. The constant of gravity is G.

the plumb line does not point straight up, but points away from the mountain, because the bob is attracted toward it. We measure the force exerted by the mountain and estimate the mass of the mountain by measuring its size and composition. Since the distance to the mountain is measurable,

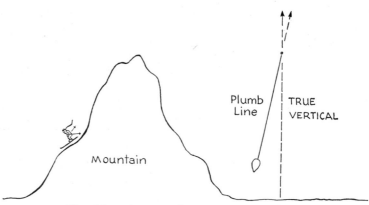

Fig. 35.—A mountain attracts a plumb bob.

The direction of the plumb line deviates from the vertical, to provide a measure of the mountain's gravitational force.

we can calculate the constant of gravity, and hence the mass of the Earth.

The mountain method is fairly good but less accurate than laboratory methods. With exceedingly delicate instruments the attraction of a large ball of lead upon a smaller ball can be directly measured (giving a value for the constant of gravity). Since the weight of the small ball measures the Earth's attraction for it, the mass of the Earth is then determined in terms of the mass of the large ball, by means of the inverse square law of the attractions. If the Earth could be put on scales at the surface, it would weigh 6,600,000,000,000,000,000,000 tons or 1.32×10^{25} pounds.

The force of gravitation is nothing but a small deviation from no force at all, becoming appreciable only when huge quantities of matter are involved. Suppose a ball were made of all the gold that has been mined in the world, say 30,000 tons; the ball would be about 46 feet in diameter. If it were placed in space, away from other attracting forces, a 200 pound man sitting on it would weigh the equivalent of $\frac{1}{100}$ of an ounce on the Earth. A cricket could easily lift him and a frog could kick him completely away from the ball of gold. Since men are not usually so easily diverted from gold we may conclude, in the manner of Aesop, that the force of avarice greatly exceeds that of gravitation.

THE MASSIVE SUN

Knowing the mass of the Earth we can now calculate the mass of the Sun. The Earth continually falls towards the Sun, away from the straight line that it would follow if there were no gravitational attraction. The amount of fall is about $\frac{1}{8}$ inches every second, in which time the Earth moves forward about 18.5 miles. The mass of the Sun required to make the Earth fall at this rate is about 332,000 times the mass of the Earth, or some 4.38×10^{30} pounds (4,380,000,000,000,000,000,000,000,000,000 lbs.).

With this knowledge of the mass of the Sun we may deduce some interesting information about its constitution. The average density is only 1.41,* while the Earth's density is 5.5, equivalent to a mixture of rock and metals. At the

---

* The density of water is taken as unity.

surface of the Sun the force of gravity is twenty-eight times as great as on the Earth. A 200 pound man would weigh nearly three tons there, except that he would evaporate instantly at the temperature of 10,000°F. From only three known quantities—mass, diameter and surface temperature—it is possible to prove that the Sun is a *gas* throughout. The temperature at the center must be about 35,000,000°F., to provide enough pressure to keep the outer gaseous layers from collapsing. No known element can be a solid or a liquid in any part of the Sun; even tungsten, used in electric light filaments, would evaporate on the surface, which is relatively cool. *

Fig. 36.—Center of gravity

is the point of balance. The figure is accurately drawn for two balls of equal density connected by a weightless rod.

A Planet with a Satellite

For a planet with a satellite, the method of determining the mass is like that used in finding the Sun's mass. The attraction of the planet must always exactly balance the centrifugal force, the rate at which the satellite falls toward the planet to remain in its orbit. With a knowledge of this attraction, the distance of the satellite, and the constant of gravitation we calculate the mass of the planet. We know the mass of Neptune, twenty-seven hundred million miles away, as accurately as we know the mass of the Moon, distant only 239,000 miles.

---

* For a complete discussion of the Sun, see "Our Sun," by Donald H. Menzel, Harvard Books on Astronomy.

WEIGHING THE MOON

The mass of a satellite is difficult to determine, because it is generally so small compared to the mass of the primary planet. The effect of the Earth on the Moon's motion is easily measured, but the Moon is so small in mass that it affects the Earth's motion only slightly. The center of the Earth moves about their common center of gravity in a very small orbit, identical in shape with that of the Moon. If the Earth and Moon could be joined by a weightless rod and the rod balanced on a knife-edge under a constant gravity, the knife-edge could support the rod at their center

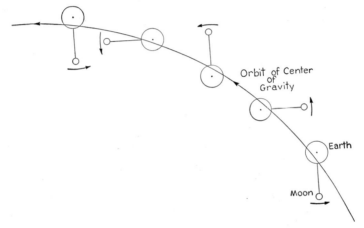

Fig. 37.—Motion of the Earth

about the center of gravity of the Earth and Moon. The center of gravity moves in a smooth ellipse about the Sun. The dimensions are exaggerated, but the relative positions of the Earth's center are correct.

of gravity (see Figure 36). It is this point that moves in a smooth elliptic orbit about the Sun. By carefully observing the distance of the center of gravity from the center of the Earth, we can measure the mass of the Moon (Figure 37). The ratio of the little orbit of the Earth's center to the larger orbit of the Moon is the ratio of the Moon's mass to that of the Earth.

The center of gravity is about 3000 miles from the center of the Earth, so that the mass of the Moon is only $1/81.56$ (or about $3000 \div 239,000$) the mass of the Earth. With such a small mass, only $81,000,000,000,000,000,000$ tons, the Moon is as tiny a part of the entire solar system as one drop of water in a fifty gallon barrel, or as the proverbial fly on a cartwheel. The Earth is merely 81.56 times as important—except to us.

OTHER SATELLITES

Only a few of the larger satellites of Jupiter and Saturn produce sufficient gravitational effects for their masses to be determined. Jupiter's four bright satellites and Titan of Saturn's system are comparable to the Moon. The other satellites are generally much less massive except for Neptune's, which appears to be larger than the Moon, although its mass is difficult to determine.

The Moon is about 3.3 times the density of water, as though made of ordinary rock. Three of the bright satellites of Jupiter are slightly less dense: one,* however, is only 0.6 as dense as water. Its possible composition will be discussed in Chapter 10. The relative masses of the various satellites are represented by spheres of a constant density in Figure 38. For some whose diameters only are known the densities were taken as 2.0, and the satellites are designated by question marks. Masses that were estimated from brightness alone are similarly designated. The range in mass is so great that it was necessary to magnify some of the diameters by a factor of ten or a hundred to make them visible on the diagram.

---

* Callisto, number four in order from Jupiter.

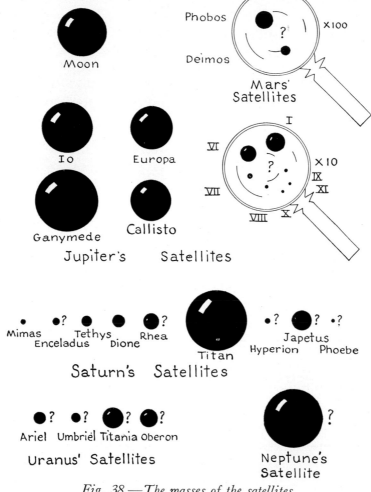

Fig. 38.—The masses of the satellites

in the solar system are depicted by spheres of constant density. Uncertain masses are designated by a question mark. The magnifications are in terms of diameters. Neptune's satellite may be more massive than is indicated. The satellites are placed in the order of their distances from their respective primaries.

Deimos and Phobos, the Lilliputian satellites of Mars, are seen to be pitiful featherweights as compared to the average satellites. The surface gravities of these small satellites are trifling. A man on one of them would weigh only a few ounces, and would be capable of jumping several miles, if not completely off the satellite. His greatest difficulty would be to move freely, without hopping upward for miles into space.

THE MASSES OF THE PLANETS

The masses of planets without satellites can be calculated only from their observed perturbations on the motions of the other planets, by a method similar to the one used in predicting the positions of Neptune and Pluto. Venus, for example, approaches the Earth, Mars and Mercury fairly closely, and produces perturbations in their motions. Similarly, the motion of Venus is perturbed by the attractions of the Earth, Mars and Mercury. The numerical solution for the masses of Venus and Mercury from observations of their motions and those of the Earth and Mars is exceedingly complicated. It has been successfully carried out, although a repetition of some of the work might be advisable at the present time.

Even with theories based on the best observations, the mass of Mercury is not very well known. Mercury is so small and so near the Sun that its effects on the other planets is barely measurable. The best analyses indicate that Mercury has only $\frac{1}{24}$ the mass of the Earth, or about three times that of the Moon. Mercury resembles the Moon in density too. It would make a very fine satellite for the Earth if a transfer could be effected—but then Mercury would suffer such a great loss in prestige, while the Moon would make only a puny planet.

The mass of Venus was mentioned in the first chapter; it is only slightly less than that of the Earth—81 per cent. All of the other planets, with the exception of Pluto, have satellites to expedite the calculation of their masses. The case of Pluto is an especially difficult one, chiefly because accurate astronomy is so young and because the outer planets move so slowly. Neptune, whose motion we should expect to be the most affected by Pluto, has been observed through much less than one revolution about the Sun. Until the orbit has been closed by at least one complete revolution it will be very difficult to determine the slight effects of Pluto's attraction reflected in Neptune's rate of motion. A fortunate set of circumstances, however, enabled Professor Dirk Brouwer, of the Yale Observatory, to apply an ingenious method in determining Pluto's mass.

Since the *rate* of Neptune's motion does not give a good solution for Pluto's attraction, Brouwer has been able to find the attraction by studying small deviations in the *direction* of Neptune's motion. He could do this because Pluto's orbit is so highly inclined to the average plane of the other planets. During the years since Neptune's discovery, Pluto has been sufficiently distant from the plane of Neptune's orbit to attract the planet appreciably in a direction *perpendicular* to the orbit. As a consequence, Pluto has forced Neptune out of its average plane by 0.9 of a second of arc, a determinate quantity because of the many observations. Brouwer found that Pluto's mass must consequently equal about 0.8 that of the Earth; hence Pluto belongs among the terrestrial planets, together with Mercury, Venus, Earth and Mars.

Figure 39 shows the masses of the planets as balls of constant density. For comparison with Figure 38, we recall that Mercury just surpasses the Moon in mass. Therefore the sequence of masses from the least satellite, Phobos, to the greatest planet, Jupiter, is fairly uniform. We might extend the sequence to the smaller bodies, such as the asteroids and meteors, without loss of uniformity, but not in the other direction. The step in diameter from Jupiter to the Sun is a factor of ten, because the Sun is a thousand times more massive.

It would unduly burden this story to describe all of the other ingenious methods that have been used in calculating or estimating the masses of planets, satellites, comets or asteroids. Whenever two bodies are observed to come near

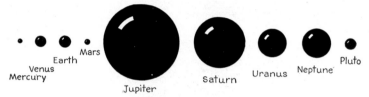

Fig. 39.—The masses of the planets.

Represented by spheres of constant density. The Sun's diameter, on this scale, should exceed Jupiter's by a factor of ten.

enough together for one to perturb the motion of the other, additional information about the masses can be determined. If close approaches occur without any observed changes in motion, an *upper limit* to the masses can be deduced. When Brooks' comet, in 1866, came within the orbits of Jupiter's inner satellites, the comet's period of revolution about the Sun was changed from twenty-nine years to seven years, yet no change was observable in the motions of the satellites. The comet, consequently, must have possessed less than 1/10,000 of the Earth's mass, or it would have produced measurable perturbations. There is no direct method of estimating a lower limit.

In concluding these chapters that involve Newton's law of gravitation, we note that the whole foundation of astronomy rests on applications of the law. Outside the solar system, in the far reaches of the universe, the law is still the key to the solution of many of the most important problems. Almost no calculations of mass can be made without using the property of attraction. There is, however, evidence that Newton's law is only a first approximation; that fast moving bodies increase their mass with speed. Einstein's theory of relativity gives the correcting factors which are just appreciable in the case of Mercury's rapid motion under the Sun's great attraction. Solely in this instance are these corrections great enough to be detectable in present day observations of the motions of celestial bodies.

Again, over truly incredible distances in space, a different correction seems to be necessary; the universe appears to be expanding. If far enough apart, masses appear to exert a repulsive force even greater than the attractive force of gravitation. Just why repulsion should occur is not clear, but various theories have been proposed to account for it. The expansion of the universe must clearly have a deep rooted cause, one that carries us to the heart of the infinite.

Since there can be no absolute in truth, each new conclusion leading on to the possibility of more general ones, we can well admire the simplicity and perfection of Newton's law, which applies so exactly. To make progress, however, the scientist must search for tiny imperfections in a law or theory that seems to be perfect.

5

THE EARTH

Our Earth seems so large, so substantial and so much with us, that we tend to forget the minor position it occupies in the solar family of planets. Only by a small margin is it the largest of the other similar planets. True, it does possess

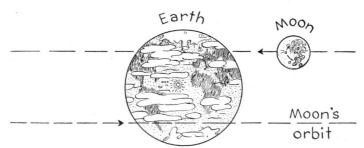

Fig. 40.—The Earth and Moon.

A telescopic view from Venus. Note the Sun's reflection in the Atlantic Ocean. The Moon's orbit would extend on each side ten times the length of the orbital lines. (*Original drawing by Donald A. MacRae.*)

a moderately thick atmosphere that overlies a thin patchy layer of water and it does have a noble satellite, about one fourth its diameter. The pair, as viewed from a suitable position in space, say from Venus as in Figure 40, would

Fig. 41.—The Earth illuminates the Moon.

When nearly new, the Moon is lighted by earthshine. (*Photograph by the Harvard Observatory.*)

undoubtedly provide an inspiring sight. These qualifications of the Earth, however, are hardly sufficient to bolster our cosmic egotism. But, small as is the Earth astronomically, it is our best known planet, and therefore deserves careful study.

Unfortunately there are no large mirrors in space to empower us to see ourselves as others might see us. There is, nevertheless, one very poor approximation to the mirror in space—the dark side of the new Moon. At this phase of the Moon, when it lies almost in a line with the Sun, the light reflected from the Earth illuminates the otherwise unlighted black hemisphere (see Figure 41). Measures of the earthshine on the Moon indicate that the Earth is a good reflector of light, as are the other planets with atmospheres. The Earth, therefore, when viewed from outer space must be a bright planet, almost as bright as Venus.

Whether an outside observer could recognize the continents is somewhat uncertain, but surely in time, by carefully plotting the positions of all the surface features, he would find that the huge cloudbanks moved and changed, while certain areas remained fixed. In this way, he could eventually plot a fairly good map. On the other hand, certain regions of almost incessant cloudiness might well be mistaken for peculiar, bright, fixed markings. The polar caps would certainly be easily recognized, and their seasonal changes delineated. During the winter season in the northern hemisphere, the polar cap would grow to cover an enormous area, some 50 degrees from the pole, while in summer the area would shrink to only a few degrees of latitude. The lower border would always be very irregular, particularly where it was broken by the oceans. The southern polar cap would change very much less, because of the scarcity of land. The seasonal changes from green, to brown, to black and white in the temperate zones could probably be recognized, and their causes explained by a clever observer.

One peculiarity that we cannot observe on any other planet could be seen by our hypothetical astronomer outside the Earth. He would be able to observe the *direct reflection* of the Sun from our oceans, when the Earth was properly turned (Figure 40). The phenomenon might be a great surprise for a Martian astronomer, who had never encountered large bodies of water. He might very well attribute the bright pointlike reflection to a smooth crystalline surface on the Earth, as the early astronomers visualized the Moon to be a perfect crystal sphere.

One observation about the planet Earth, as recorded by an outside astronomer in his book of facts, would be that the poles of rotation are not perpendicular to the ecliptic, the plane of revolution about the Sun. By long and careful measures he would conclude that the equator is tipped $23\frac{1}{2}$ degrees from the plane of the ecliptic. This *obliquity of the ecliptic* might enable him to account for the seasonal

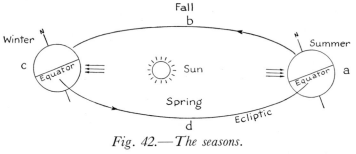

Fig. 42.—*The seasons.*

Winter and summer are both moderated in the northern hemisphere and accentuated in the southern hemisphere by the eccentric position of the Sun. The seasons, labeled for the North, are reversed for the South.

changes of color in the temperature zones and the variation in the sizes of the polar caps.

He would conclude that the direction of the poles remains fixed in space as the Earth moves in its orbit about the Sun, as in Figure 42. When the north pole was tipped towards the Sun (*a*), that hemisphere would be more illuminated by the Sun's rays. The pole would be lighted continuously, and the length of the day would be greater everywhere north of the equator. In addition, the light would fall on the surface at an angle more nearly perpendicular so that an area would receive more heat and light during the daylight (Figure 43), and would have more hours of sunlight.

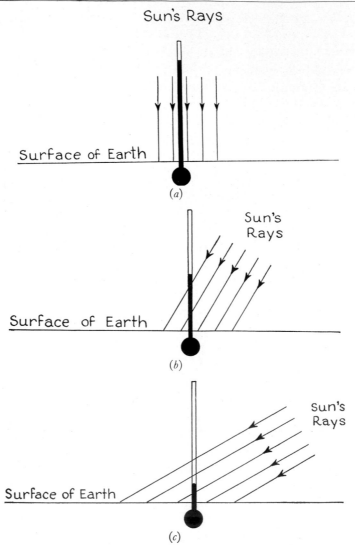

Sun's Rays

Surface of Earth

(a)

Sun's Rays

Surface of Earth

(b)

Sun's Rays

Surface of Earth

(c)

Fig. 43.—The Sun heats a surface

more effectively when the rays fall vertically as in (*a*), rather than obliquely as in (*b*) or (*c*).

A quarter of the period later (three months) the Earth would be in the position (*b*, Figure 42), and everywhere the hours of daylight would equal those of darkness. During the next half period (six months) the southern hemisphere would gain in heat while the northern hemisphere would lose, the north pole being completely dark during that time. If our outside astronomer possessed any ingenuity at all (and of course he must, being an astronomer!), he would be able to explain completely the observed changes in color in the two hemispheres, and also the peculiarities in the changes of the polar caps. He might express himself as follows: "Clearly, on the planet Earth, there must be complicated chemical or physical reactions that are directly activated by solar heat. Some regions, the dark blue areas that comprise most of the planet's surface, are affected only by very great variations in heat, while other regions, those that turn green as the temperature rises, are affected by much smaller changes. The permanent polar caps are probably similar to those regions that turn green with increase of temperature, but are never heated sufficiently for the reaction to occur."

Our learned friend from outside might continue, "We must conclude, therefore, that the more stable dark blue areas are very good conductors of heat as compared to those unstable areas which are so affected by slight changes etc. . . . " Since the present writer is not too certain as to the remainder of the weighty conclusions, we may well let the matter drop at this point. The observations from outside would be of much more interest than the conclusions.

The time of highest temperature would be observed not to occur at the time of greatest length of day and of maximum sunlight on the surface. In the North Temperate Zone the maximum sunlight falls near June 21 (point *a* in Figure 42), but midsummer, the time of highest temperature, comes actually late in July or near the first of August (in North America). The other seasons are correspondingly late. The seasons *lag* because the surface of the Earth (only the upper few feet and the atmosphere) becomes warmer as the amount of heat received from the Sun increases. The temperature continues to rise as long as the heat is strong, even though it is beginning to wane, until the rate of gain equals the rate of loss. Similarly, the coldest winter weather comes a month or more after December 21, the shortest day of the year.

It is interesting to note that the Earth is at perihelion, nearest to the Sun, during midwinter in the northern hemisphere, and at aphelion, farthest away, during midsummer. The effect is to moderate the seasons slightly in the northern hemisphere, but to increase the range in temperature slightly in the southern hemisphere, where the effect is reversed.

The Earth is generally called a sphere but actually is not a perfect one. Careful measures show that the diameter at the equator is about 27 miles* greater than the diameter at the poles; the actual shape is similar to that of a door knob, though almost spherical. This deformation does not arise by chance; the Earth was not cast in that shape to remain so forever. The internal gravitation is great enough to draw the material of the Earth into a more nearly perfect sphere, were there no rotation. The rotation in 24 hours, however, causes a centrifugal force that enlarges the equatorial diameter at the expense of the polar diameter, to produce the observed equatorial bulge. If the underlying material of the Earth were too rigid to take the form prescribed by the rota-

---

* One part in 297.

tion, the water in the oceans would flow to the equator to compensate the centrifugal force (Figure 44a). Since the

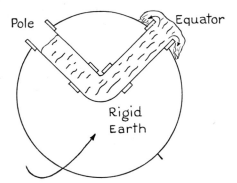

Fig. 44a.—A rigid spherical Earth

in rotation would spill water out of a pipe from the pole to the equator. Although no such pipe exists, the oceans, correspondingly, would flow to the equator.

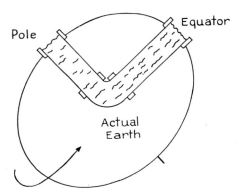

Fig. 44b.—The actual Earth

in rotation, bulges at the equator, and maintains a uniform water level between the pole and the equator.

oceans are not particularly deeper there than elsewhere on the globe, we must conclude that the "solid" Earth adjusts itself to the force (Figure 44b).

The presence of an equatorial bulge on the Earth, besides leading to such paradoxes as "The Mississippi River runs up hill," * has one effect of great importance to the astronomer. This effect is called the *precession of the equinoxes*, observed in antiquity and explained by Newton. The term precession describes the fact that the Earth's pole does not remain fixed in direction over long intervals of time, but moves slowly around with a period of about 26,000 years. The angle between the equator and the ecliptic does not change essentially, although the pole twists around like the axis of a

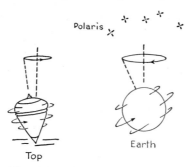

Fig. 45.—A top and the Earth.

Both precess because of forces that act to change the direction of their axes of rotation.

spinning top. The analogy (see Figure 45) is almost perfect, for the Earth really acts as a huge top.

The axis of the top is the polar axis of the Earth, the main body of the top is the Earth, while the rim of the top is the equatorial bulge. Because of the obliquity of the ecliptic, the bulge is always being attracted by the Moon, Sun and planets, which try to turn the bulge, and therefore the equator, into the plane of the ecliptic. In the case of the top, the action of gravity is the reverse, to overturn the axis of rotation. In neither case does the overturning force succeed in causing the spinning body to tip over. Instead, the angle between the spin and the force remains the same but the axis precesses around as shown in

---

* The mouth of the river is farther from the center of the Earth than the source. The river flows because of the centrifugal force of the rotation.

Figure 45.* The peculiar property of a spinning body to resist a force applied to the axis is exemplified in the gyroscope, an instrument whose most important use is in gyrocompasses and in stabilizers for ships or airplanes.

The precession of the equinoxes ceases to be a purely academic problem when we look into the complications that it produces in calendar making. Back in Figure 42 we see that the time of the seasons will depend on the direction of the Earth's pole. When the Earth and Sun are on the line of the *equinoxes* (b or d), where the planes of the equator and ecliptic intersect, the season will be either Spring or Fall. The precession of the equinoxes is a westward† motion of the equinoxes as measured with respect to the stars. If the year were defined as one revolution of the Earth about the Sun, as measured with respect to the stars, the seasons would soon begin to get out of step, and within a few thousand years would be entirely changed. To avoid such a difficulty the calendar year, or *tropical* year, is measured from the time that the Sun is in the direction of the *vernal* (Spring) equinox until it has returned there again. This tropical‡ year keeps the calendar in step with the seasons but is shorter than the true, *sidereal*, year by about 20 minutes.

---

* The only difference between the actions of the Earth and of the top is that the disturbing force is opposite in direction. Consequently, the directions of precession are opposite. Anyone who has experimented with a gyroscope will have observed how the motion of the axis of rotation is always perpendicular to the direction of the disturbing force applied to it.

† Clockwise when one looks down from the direction of the north pole.

‡ The length of the tropical year is 365 d. 5 h. 48 m. 46.0 s. The leap year troubles of calendar making arise from the fraction of a day left over the 365 d.

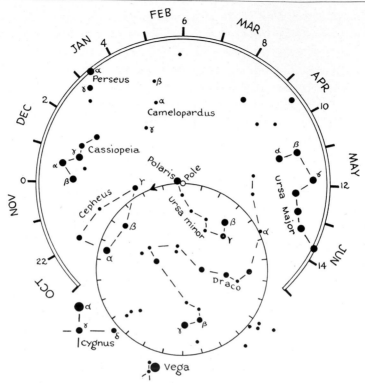

Fig. 46.—Vega will be the pole star in 14,000 A.D.

because of the precession of the equinoxes. Over a period of nearly 26,000 years, the Earth's pole follows the smaller circle among the stars. Each mark represents 1000 years. This chart may be used for identifying polar constellations. Turn it so that correct month is uppermost and face North for observations near 8 P. M. (*Chart by Donald A. MacRae.*)

The ancient astronomers noticed the phenomenon that the position of the stars in the sky at the same season shifted slowly with time,* and also the more obvious phenomenon

---

* One cycle comprised the "Year of the Gods." To these deities a man's life span was as a day is to a man. The period of the precession is quite closely 70×365 years.

that the north pole of the Earth was shifting. Polaris, our present pole star, is only temporarily useful as such (see Figure 46), though the motion of the pole in a lifetime is negligible. At the time when the Pyramids of Egypt were constructed, the pole star was α Draconis, some 25 degrees from Polaris. The Southern Cross (a southern constellation) could then have been observed from most of the land that now comprises the United States.

To the astronomer the precession of the equinoxes presents many more serious difficulties than are involved in a mere change of the length of the year. He is forced to make his measures of celestial objects with respect to a reference system that does not remain fixed. His plight resembles that of an imaginary map maker, who finds that all the continents and islands of the world are moving about. To state the latitude and longitude on one of them would require a calculation involving the desired instant of time. Similarly, in astronomy, the starting point for practical measures is the vernal equinox, and the fundamental plane is the equator. Since these primary directions are moving because of precession, every published measure of a star or planet must carry with it the date, in order that anyone using the observation will know the directions of the equinox and equator at that instant.

The motions of the Earth cause two additional complications in the problem of recording directions on the sky. One of these, *nutation*, is a small periodic irregularity in the precession, caused by the Moon's peculiar motions and varying attraction on the equatorial bulge. The main effect of nutation is an oscillation in the motion of the pole over a period of about nineteen years. Only the most complicated mathematical theory enables the astronomer to calculate all of the small disturbances that finally add together in producing precession and nutation. Professor F. R. Moulton expresses his admiration for the work in this field by saying, "No words can give an adequate conception of the intricacy or the beauty of the mathematical theory of nutation."*

The second complication in observing the celestial bodies is the effect known as the *aberration* of light. Aberration was first observed and explained by the English Astronomer Royal, James Bradley, about 1728. The story is one of the many fine examples of an exciting type of scientific research, in which one phenomenon is sought and an unexpected one found. To prove that the Earth revolves about the Sun, Bradley attempted to observe the parallactic shift of the stars as the Earth moves about its orbit. He set his telescope very rigidly in a well-built (but disused) chimney, in order to watch the daily passage of a certain star. If the Earth really revolved about the Sun, the position at each passage should have changed slightly during the year.

Painstaking observations failed to prove the motion of the Earth directly, but did show a displacement out of phase with the one Bradley expected. He finally explained the new effect as due to the combined result of the motion of the Earth and the finite velocity of light.

There is a well-known story that the explanation came to Bradley while he was sailing on the Thames River. The vane on the masthead of the boat changed its direction as the boat changed its course, although the wind remained steady from one direction. If we imagine the wind as being light from a star, the boat as our moving Earth, and the vane as a telescope pointing in the apparent direction of the star, we can see that the direction of the star will depend upon the motion of the Earth. In Figure 47, where a telescope and incoming light ray are shown, one can see that the motion of the telescope while the light is passing through will necessi-

---

* *Astronomy*, New York: Macmillan, 1931, p. 124.

tate that the telescope be tilted forward, in order to prevent the light ray from striking the sides of the tube.

A good example of aberration is the everyday experience of holding an umbrella ahead when walking in the rain. Drops that actually fall vertically may strike the body if one walks too fast. When light falls upon the Earth from a star, the change in direction by aberration is small, about 20 seconds of arc, but great enough that all observations of

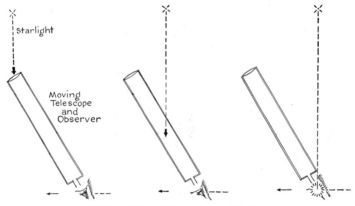

Starlight

Moving
Telescope
and
Observer

Fig. 47.—Aberration of light.

A moving observer must tip his telescope forward in order that the moving light ray will move centrally through the tube.

celestial bodies must be corrected for it. The velocity of the Earth is only 18.5 miles per second, as compared to the velocity of light, 186,000 miles per second. The ratio of these two velocities corresponds to the aberration angle.*

It is noteworthy that Bradley succeeded also in discovering nutation, but never did attain his original goal of directly proving the motion of the Earth by the parallactic shifts of the stars. More than a hundred years of telescopic improvements were necessary before this result was attained. Brad-

* Its tangent.

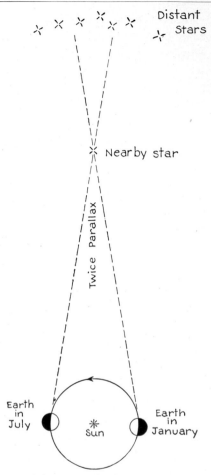

Fig. 48.—Stellar parallax.

The parallax of a star is the angle of the radius of the Earth's orbit as seen from the star. The angle in the diagram represents twice the parallax of the star. The parallax can be directly measured for only the nearer stars because it becomes undetectable for the more distant ones.

ley's proof of the Earth's revolution about the Sun was, nevertheless, a good one, despite the fact that it was not the proof he had expected to find.

Not until 1838 was the direct effect of the Earth's revolution observed. Friedrich Wilhelm Bessel was able to measure a slight shift in the position of the star 61 Cygni as it changed direction when seen from opposite parts of the Earth's orbit. The stellar parallax (Figure 48), is three tenths of a second of arc, i.e., the astronomical unit would appear to subtend an angle of three tenths of a second as seen from 61 Cygni. The nearest star now known is Proxima Centauri, for which the parallax is $0''76$. The distance in miles is directly calculated as $\frac{1}{0.76} \times 206,265 \times 92,870,000$ or 2.51×10^{13} miles.

Such a distance is too great to be visualized but is better expressed in terms of a light-year, the distance that light (moving 186,000 miles per second) travels in a year. Light comes to us from the Moon in 1.3 seconds, from the Sun in 8.5 minutes, but from Proxima Centauri it requires more than *four years*. Even the bright stars, visible to the naked eye, are much more remote. The most distant star that can be photographed with the 100-inch telescope at Mount Wilson is more than ten million light years away, while the faintest *island universe** of stars is distant by several *hundred million* light years. We can scarcely criticize the ancient astronomers for not anticipating these enormous distances.

The motion of the Earth is considered today, not as the ponderous movement of a huge mass through space, but as the natural movement of a small planet about an average star. In the depths of space the Earth counts for little more than a dust speck. To its inhabitants, however, the Earth is home, the Mother Planet, and is justifiably the most important member of the universe. In the next chapter we shall see how good a home it actually provides.

---

* Spiral nebula or external galaxy.

6

THE EARTH AS AN ABODE FOR LIFE

THE EARTH IS TAKEN FOR GRANTED BY THE MAJORITY OF ITS inhabitants. There is, of course, some grumbling about the bad weather, the poor crops, or the occasional catastrophes, but generally no critical analysis. Such an attitude is justified by the fact that there is no alternative; having been born on the Earth we have no choice but to accept what hospitality it may offer. We are forced by circumstance into a situation from which there is no escape; let us make the most of it.

From a broader viewpoint, however, it is interesting to speculate on the permanency of our dwelling, the dangers lurking in space, the possibilities of local or worldwide catastrophes, and the unique conditions required for the maintenance of the fragile force we call *life*.

Let us first consider the dangers from without. For the existence of life as we know it, the temperature must, some of the time, rise above the freezing point of water but must never exceed the boiling point. This restriction on the conditions of temperature is more limited than it seems at first glance, because the temperature scale begins at absolute zero, $-460°F.$, and rises indefinitely. The highest temperatures directly observed are some hundreds of thousands of degrees, while the interiors of the stars possess temperatures of many millions of degrees.

The Sun provides the Earth with the necessary heat for maintaining a suitable temperature range, only 180 degrees out of millions, and does not raise the temperature too high. Evidence from the past indicates that the Sun has not *greatly* changed its output of heat for some hundreds of millions of years, and the best theories of the source of the Sun's energy indicate that it will probably continue to shine much as it does now for as long into the future.* However, a slight change of only a few per cent in the Sun's heat, would produce violent changes in the climate of the Earth. There is no assurance that small changes of this order might not occur at any time, although the average heat over long periods of time may remain constant.

The Earth's atmosphere is a vital agent in maintaining a suitable temperature. It acts as a blanket to keep the noon temperature from rising too high and the night temperature from falling too low. Exactly as the glass in a greenhouse transmits the visual light of the sun but holds the heat, or far infrared light, to maintain a higher temperature than exists outside, so the atmosphere maintains a temperature balance near the surface of the Earth.

On the Moon, for example, where there is no atmosphere, the midday temperature surpasses the boiling point of water and the night temperature falls to about $-240°F.$, much below the melting point of "dry ice." In space, outside the atmosphere of the Earth, the temperature in the shade

---

* The energy of the Sun arises not from any burning process but probably from the transformation of hydrogen into helium, in part by a complicated process involving carbon and nitrogen. There is apparently enough hydrogen left to supply the Sun for some *ten thousand million years.*

approximates the absolute zero, so that a heat-regulating atmosphere would be requisite to any active form of life in space.

Fig. 49.—A meteor flashes across the field of a telescope.
(*Photograph by the Harvard Observatory.*)

The atmosphere, moreover, is a roof of protection from much more than the extremes of temperature. It is a most invaluable shield from the meteors continually bombarding the Earth from interplanetary space (see Figure 49). These meteors move at velocities up to 45* miles per second. A

---

* The velocity of escape from the solar system.

meteoric particle weighing only 1/30,000 of an ounce ($\frac{1}{1000}$ gram), moving at this speed, would strike with the same energy and be as lethal as a direct discharge from a 45-caliber pistol fired at point-blank range. Such a particle would be no larger than a fair-sized speck of dust, much smaller than an average grain of sand, yet as dangerous to a person as the pistol bullet. Thousands of millions of such particles strike the Earth's atmosphere daily, as faint meteors

Fig. 50.—The Arizona Meteor Crater.
(*Photograph by Clyde Fisher.*)

that can be seen only with a telescope. The meteors visible to the naked eye are several times greater. In the atmosphere these bodies are immediately vaporized by friction with the air.

It is indeed fortunate that we are shielded from the meteors, but even so, some of the more massive ones are able to penetrate to the surface of the Earth and produce damage. The Great Meteor Crater in Arizona, Figure 50, was formed by the explosion of such a huge body from space. This crater is nearly a mile in diameter and even now is nearly six hundred feet deep, despite infilling by erosion.

Small meteorites have been found in abundance around the crater but no large ones have been discovered either by drilling operations or by radio-detection apparatus. The meteoritic body probably exploded at impact, with a force far exceeding that of any known explosives. Only the "shrapnel" and the crater are left to tell us the story. The Great Siberian meteor of 1908 detonated so violently that trees were laid flat over a radius of 25 miles from the area of

Fig. 51.—The Great Siberian meteor

devastated the forest over a distance of twenty-five miles from the point of fall. (*Photograph by L. A. Kulik.*)

impact (Figure 51). Should another meteor comparable to these occur in a large city, the damage would be incalculable. Our only protection from such devastating meteors lies in their extreme rarity, but there is always the remote possibility that a stream of them might be encountered at any time (see Figure 52).

Our atmosphere not only protects us from smaller meteors, it also guards us from death-dealing radiations in space. Light in the near ultraviolet causes sunburn but is generally important for health, although not a necessity. The ozone,* formed by the Sun's light, constitutes a shield from the rays of shorter wave length farther into the ultraviolet, where the rays begin to become dangerous to health. The oxygen,

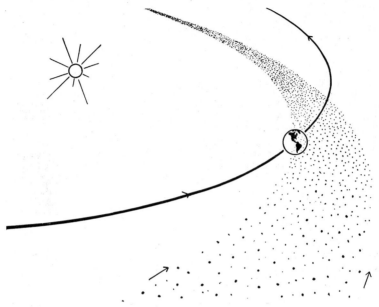

Fig. 52.—Stream of meteors.

Moving in an elliptic orbit about the Sun. Such a stream, often composed of cometary remnants, produces a meteor shower. (*By P. M. Millman. Courtesy of "The Telescope Magazine."*)

nitrogen and other elements in the atmosphere cut out all of the far ultraviolet rays below the limit of ozone. These rays are used medically to *kill* bacteria in the air. Could they *all* reach the Earth it is doubtful that life in any form could exist.

---

* Produces the odor around electric discharges. Ozone contains three atoms of oxygen per molecule.

Fig. 53.—The aurora borealis or northern lights.

These displays are produced in the Earth's atmosphere by streams of electrons and atoms sent out by the Sun. (*Photograph by Carl Störmer. Courtesy "Archives des Sciences," Genève.*)

Besides the far ultraviolet rays, many particles that would be dangerous to life are stopped by the atmosphere. These particles, positive and negative in charge, emanate both from the Sun and from space in general. The streams of charged particles that cause the northern lights, or *aurorae borealis*, come from the Sun (see Figure 53), while the *cosmic rays* come from unknown sources in space. It is highly probable that there are other kinds of rays and particles in space that are still unrecognized simply because our atmosphere prevents them from reaching the Earth. In the laboratory the cyclotron can now generate exceedingly dangerous streams of positively charged particles. The light from one of these streams is shown in Figure 54.

It is clear that life as we know it requires a very specific set of circumstances for its continued existence on the Earth.

Fig. 54.—The Harvard cyclotron.

The nuclei of hydrogen atoms have been accelerated to a speed of 20,000 miles per second by electrical and magnetic fields within the cyclotron. (*Photograph by Paul H. Donaldson, Cruft Laboratory, Harvard University.*)

The dangers from without specify that the planet must be within a rather definite distance of a star whose light is quite stable over long intervals of time, and the planet must possess an atmosphere capable of regulating the temperature and of screening out dangerous rays and particles.

No mention has been made of the exact composition required for the atmosphere. Until many more experiments have been made, the limits through which the composition may range without eliminating all possible forms of life is quite uncertain, but probably the limits are very broad. Oxygen for animal life, and nitrogen and carbon dioxide for plant life are essential components, while water must be available for both. (See Table I for the composition of dry air.) Surface water is not indispensable for certain desert plants but water, in some form, is necessary for all life as we know it. The formation of chemical compounds in the early stages of a planet's formation first determines the composition of the atmosphere. More oxygen, for example, is combined in the rocks of the Earth's surface than exists in the air. When life becomes prevalent, the chemical reac-

TABLE 1

COMPOSITION OF AIR †

Element	Per Cent by Volume
Nitrogen	78.08
Oxygen	20.94
Argon	0.94
Carbon Dioxide	0.03
Hydrogen	0.01
Neon	0.0012
Helium	0.0004
(Water Vapor	0.0 to 2.6)

† W. J. Humphreys, *Physics of the Air*, New York: McGraw-Hill, 1940.

tions of the life processes affect the atmospheric composition; plants absorb carbon dioxide and give up oxygen while for animals the process is reversed.

In recent years, consensus favors the theory that the atmosphere has practically a uniform composition to very high levels (perhaps 60 miles), because of the high prevailing winds and convection currents at these altitudes. Winds of 100 miles per hour and greater are observed in the meteor trains and the strange high clouds* at altitudes even

---

* The noctilucent clouds, observed chiefly near the arctic twilight zones.

Fig. 55.—A meteorological balloon.

This balloon will report on stratospheric conditions by short-wave radio. (*Photograph by C. A. Brooks of the Blue Hill Meteorological Observatory of Harvard University.*)

above 50 miles. Such strong winds probably mix the air sufficiently to prevent the light gases, such as hydrogen, from stratifying at the top. There are now several methods of estimating the density and temperature of the air at great altitudes. The methods are complicated, depending upon speeds of sound waves from gunfire and violent explosions such as the Siberian meteorite, upon the resistance of the air to meteors and upon the reflections of radio waves.

At low altitudes, up to about 20 miles, the temperature can be directly measured by sending up small balloons with light meteorological equipment. These balloons carry tiny radio transmitters which send down messages of temperature, pressure, etc., while their heights are being observed with telescopes from two or more ground stations. One of

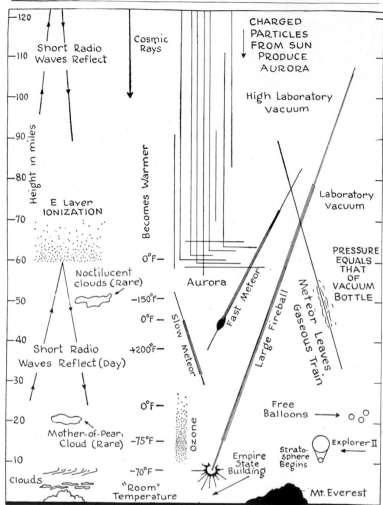

Fig. 56.—Phenomena in the upper atmosphere.
(Original drawing by Donald A. MacRae.)

these balloons is shown ready for flight in Figure 55. At heights above 20 miles indirect methods of determining temperature must be used. The best estimates of temperatures at various levels are shown in Figure 56, likewise some of the phenomena that appear at these levels.

There is, so far, no explanation of the zone of high temperature (about the boiling point of water) near a height of 40 miles, though probably the air is heated there by some absorption of solar radiation. Of especial interest is the rapidity with which the air density decreases with height, reaching about one millionth the surface value near a height of 60 miles. Half of the air is contained in the first $3\frac{1}{2}$ miles above the surface, half of the remainder above 8 miles etc. At the elevations where meteors are seen, radio signals are reflected, and the aurora borealis appears, the density of air is no greater than in the vacuum of a thermos bottle. A much thinner atmosphere than ours would still be a good shield from external dangers, but might not regulate the surface temperature so efficiently.

The interior of the Earth cannot, of course, be studied as easily as the atmosphere, but there are methods of learning a great deal about it. Deep wells have penetrated only two or three miles, a negligible fraction of the distance to the center. The astronomical effects from the equatorial bulge yield some information. Geological data are highly important in describing effects in the surface layers. Variations in the attraction of gravity from place to place and the strengths and directions of Earth magnetism add extremely valuable data concerning somewhat lower levels, but the most exact information about all of the layers deeper than a few miles proceeds from the manner in which earthquake (or seismic) waves travel through the Earth.

The many methods used to study the Earth are extremely ingenious and interesting, but even to describe briefly the more important ones would require no less than another book. A short outline of the results, however, will impart some impression of the Earth's construction and will demonstrate the precarious nature of the existence we enjoy on the skin of this planet.

Astronomical results give the average density (5.5 the density of water) of the Earth and its shape at the surface; the attraction of the equatorial bulge and the known densities of rocks furnish a consistent idea of the densities of the Earth near the surface—about 2.8 times the density of water, or half the mean density.

The deep wells show that the temperature generally increases with depth at an average rate of about one degree Fahrenheit in fifty feet, although the rate varies tremendously from place to place. If this temperature increase were to continue to the center of the Earth, the temperature would reach the very high value of $400,000°F$. That this temperature must be too great is shown by geophysical investigations, which place the central temperatures as low as several thousand degrees. The low heat conductivity of the surface rocks make the change of temperature with depth very rapid near the surface, while in the deep layers heat is better conducted and the temperature changes more slowly. Very high temperatures at deep levels of the Earth would destroy the magnetism which directs a compass. An additional increase of the near-surface temperatures is made by the contribution of the radioactive elements, such as thorium and radium, which seem to be concentrated largely in the Earth's crust.

It is almost universally believed that the Earth was originally a molten mass and that the present heat in the center is the residue of that which has not been able to escape since the outer layers cooled to the solid state. In the early stages, some two or three billion years ago,* the rate of loss must have been very much greater than at present, because convection currents in the liquid material would carry the heat upwards. With the formation of a solid crust the process became relatively very slow, volcanoes and lava flows carrying at most a few per cent of the whole.

Undisturbed earth

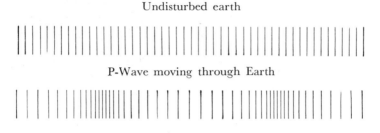

P-Wave moving through Earth

a

Undisturbed Particles in Earth

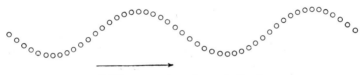

S-Wave moving through Earth

b

Fig. 57.—Earthquake waves.

The *P*-waves move by condensation and rarefaction, while the *S*-waves are transverse vibrations.

Without the information gained from the study of earthquake waves the structure of the deep interior of the Earth would be mostly conjecture. When an earthquake is produced, usually by a sudden slipping of the crustal rocks

---

* The ages of the oldest rocks are determined from measures of radioactivity residues, such as helium and certain leads.

along a fault, two main types of waves are sent out in all directions through the Earth. The P-wave, *primary* or *pressure** wave, is like a sound wave. The vibration is carried forward by a condensation of higher pressure and density, as in Figure 57*a*. The second type of vibration is the S-wave, *secondary* or *shear* wave, in which the motion is perpendicular to the direction of travel as for a light wave or a wave on the surface of water (Figure 57*b*). The P-wave, always traveling faster (approximately 1.8 times) than the S-wave, makes an earlier record of an earthquake on the seismograph at the recording station (see record in Figure 58). A few miles below the Earth's surface the P-wave travels about 5

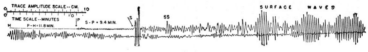

Fig. 58.—Seismogram.

Showing the nature of the record made by the various earthquake waves. The P- and S-waves precede the stronger surface waves. (*Courtesy L. Don Leet and "The Telescope Magazine."*)

miles per second and the S-wave a little less than 3 miles per second. The speeds of both waves increase at greater depths, where the densities and pressures are greater. The destructive energy of an earthquake is carried by slower surface waves, more complex in nature than the P- and S-waves.

The most remarkable result obtained from a study of the records made by these waves after they pass through various parts of the Earth, is that the S-waves do not penetrate a central core (the Dahm core), which extends slightly more than half way out from the center (see Figures 59 and 60). Since S-waves are damped out in liquids, it is thought by

---

* This name is equally descriptive and more easily remembered than the more precise name, *condensation wave*.

many geophysicists that the Earth has a *liquid* core. Whether actually liquid or not, the core differs considerably in structure from the levels above it, having a density about twice the average.

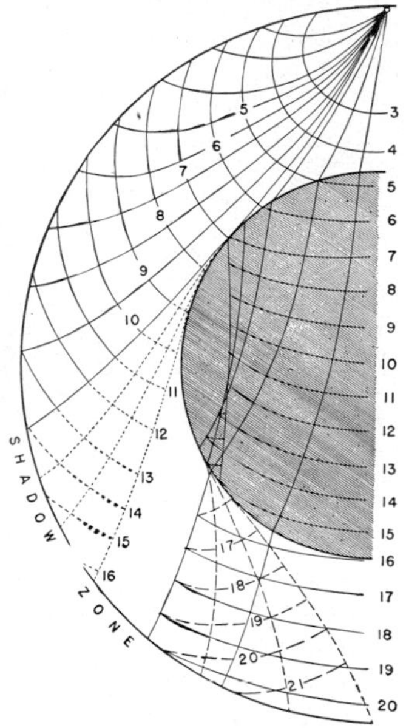

The pressures near the center of the Earth are tremendous, about 50 million pounds per square inch. It is difficult, therefore, to predict at what temperature any given material would melt or how much it would be compressed. The compression of a solid or liquid would certainly be appreciable and the melting temperature would certainly rise. Since the Earth is magnetic and since iron (and nickel-iron) is so prevalent in meteorites,* most investigators conclude that the core of the earth is made largely of iron or nickel iron. The high pressure compresses the iron from a density of 7.7, which it has on the Earth's surface, to about 10 to 12 at the center. There the P-waves travel about 7 or 8 miles per second.

Just outside the Dahm core, in the intermediate shell as seen in Figure 60, the densities are about the average for the

Fig. 59.—Shadow zone for an earthquake originating at the top of the figure. The core of the Earth refracts the P-waves and produces zones where they are not detected at the surface. The numbers represent the minutes required for the wave to reach the curved lines perpendicular to the direction of motion. The S-waves are stopped by the core. (*After Gutenberg. Courtesy L. Don Leet and "The Telescope Magazine."*)

---

* As representative of celestial bodies.

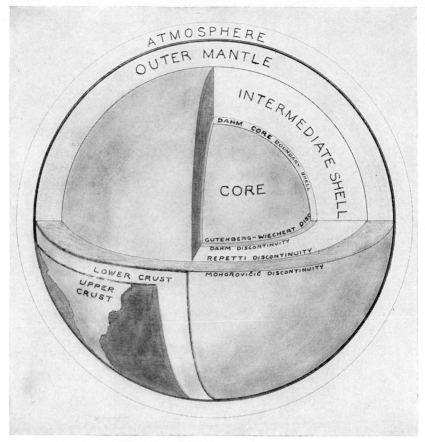

Fig. 60.—The Earth's interior.

The density increases from layer to layer towards the center. (*From Gutenberg's "Internal Constitution of the Earth," after J. B. Macelwane. Courtesy McGraw-Hill Book Co.*)

entire Earth. Some iron-stone mixture under pressure may constitute this layer. The outer mantle is somewhat denser (4.3 times water) than the heavier rocks, but may be largely composed of them. The crust consists mostly of granites and other igneous rocks, the sedimentary rocks appearing only in the upper mile or so, on the average.

The outer crust of the Earth varies in thickness from place to place and from investigator to investigator, but has an average thickness of some 30 miles. Geologically, the *crust* appears to *float* on a deformable but exceedingly viscous layer perhaps one or two hundred miles in depth. The formation of mountains, the extensive distortions of the crust, and the general demonstrations of *isostasy** show clearly that the crust is subject to motions that could not be possible unless there were an underlying layer of pseudo-liquid material that could yield. For quick acting forces, such as earthquake waves, the material is very rigid; to forces acting over long periods of time it gives way. Glass is such a material. Volcanoes show, of course, that some liquid material must exist just below the crust, but all of the deformable layer need not be liquid, in the ordinary sense.

There is some evidence that the continents have moved considerably with respect to each other in geological time (Figure 61), and that the north pole was once in the Pacific Ocean. If such is the case—the evidence is far from conclusive—the crust of the Earth has slid around the interior like the shell of an egg, † and in addition has been distorted. The chief astronomical objection to this theory rests on the fact that the pole of the Earth shows no tendency to be going anywhere at the present time. It does have a wobbling motion of a few feet, as measured by changes in the latitudes

---

* According to the principle of isostasy the total mass under any given area is constant. Lighter surface materials, such as those that form mountains, are lifted. Glaciers depress the surface, which again rises slowly after the ice melts.

† Reminiscent of the classical method of distinguishing between fresh and hard-boiled eggs without breaking the shells. A spinning fresh egg if stopped and suddenly released will start spinning again.

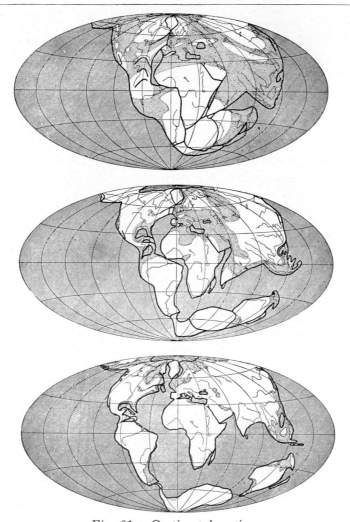

Fig. 61.—Continental motions.

According to Wegener's theory. (*From "Lehrbuch der Physik." Courtesy Friedrich Viewey und Sohn.*)

at various stations, but has not exhibited a systematic motion in any direction during the time of accurate measurement (see Figure 62).

The wobbling of the pole* is well explained by theory. The principal motion has a period of about 428 days, while there is a smaller motion in a year. Seasonal changes cause a melting and shifting of the ice in the polar caps which would

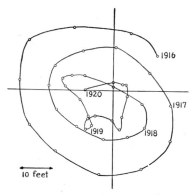

Fig. 62.—Polar motion

over the Earth's surface from 1916 to 1920. The small circles denote the position of the pole at intervals of a tenth of a year. (*After H. Spencer Jones.*)

produce a small yearly effect, but the 428-day period requires more explanation. If we again consider the Earth as a top, it is like one that was set spinning badly, not exactly about the symmetrical axis perpendicular to the plane of the equatorial bulge. Major earthquakes may also tend to displace the pole slightly and tend to change the nature of the polar wobbling. If the Earth were absolutely rigid, the pole

---

* Where the imaginary pole pierces the Earth's surface. This wobbling of the pole on the surface should not be confused with nutation, Chapter V, the wobbling of the polar direction.

would oscillate in about ten months, but as the Earth is only twice as rigid as steel, the period is 428 days, as observed.

The fragile crust of the Earth, floating on the heated and deformable rocks underneath, is not the stable and permanent layer that it appears from everyday experience. Not only is it possibly shifting about the main body of the Earth, but it is certainly cracking and buckling through geologic ages. Many regions, having become completely covered with ice in the glacial ages, sank with the load. When the ice melted, they rose again. Most of the present land areas have been under water for long periods of time, and many of the sea bottoms have been dry land. Geologists are confident that these changes always occur slowly, but their confidence is based largely upon recent experience.*

The crust is in almost continuous vibration produced by earthquakes that originate from shifts and readjustments in the various strata beneath, sometimes several hundred miles deep. Volcanoes may become active at any time, and occasionally produce catastrophic results, such as the violent explosion of Krakatau.

When we contemplate all of these dangers to life both from within and from without the Earth, we must indeed marvel that we still exist—but, of course if we did not . . .

---

* The story of an ancient devastating flood is common to many peoples, and the story of Atlantis reappears frequently.

7

THE MOON'S INFLUENCE ON THE EARTH

THE ERA IS WELL PAST WHEN MYSTICAL POWERS OF THE Moon were supposed to influence our everyday life on the Earth. No longer do thinking people attempt to credit the Moon with their successes or blame it for their failures. The Moon does, however, influence the Earth directly in many ways—all subject to simple laws of physics and dynamics.

The Moon is so large and so close to us that it reflects sufficient sunlight at its full phase to light up the night satisfactorily for many practical purposes of life. It is massive enough to distort the shape of the Earth and to produce tides in lakes and oceans. It provides the main force that moves the poles of the Earth in the precession of the equinoxes. Its distortion of the Earth's shape produces friction that slowly lengthens the hours of the day. Its shadow on the Earth at occasional places and times obscures the light of the Sun to produce solar eclipses. In such ways our nearest neighbor in space makes its presence known. To see how these effects are brought about, let us begin by investigating the motions and superficial appearance of the Moon.

The Moon's period of revolution about the Earth is approximately represented by the calendar month. Were fractional months feasible in a calendar, there should be 12.37 . . . months per year, because their average length is 29 d. 12 h. 44 m. 2.78 s. This period, technically the *synodic* month, is the space of time in which the Moon

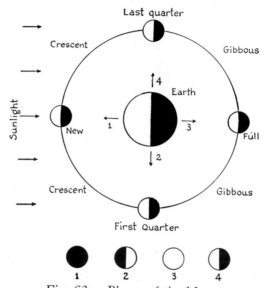

Fig. 63.—Phases of the Moon.

As seen from the Earth during one synodic month.

passes through its sequence of phases from *new* to *first quarter*, to *full*, to *third quarter* (see Figure 63), and makes a complete revolution with respect to the Sun. Since the Earth has moved forward about 30 degrees in its orbit during this time, the true or *sidereal* month, measured with respect to the stars, is a little more than two days shorter than the synodic month. On the average, a sidereal month has a length of 27 d. 7 h. 43 m. 11.47 s.

The reason for the difference in lengths of the two months can be seen from Figure 64. Starting from a new Moon (A), when the Sun, Moon and Earth are line, we see that the Moon returns to the same direction with respect to stars *before* it reaches the *new* phase again, because the Earth has completed part of its revolution about the Sun in the meantime.

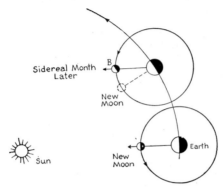

Fig. 64.—A sidereal month

is shorter than a synodic month. The Moon is not yet new again at position B, although it has completed a revolution about the Earth with respect to the stars.

The most curious fact about the Moon's motion is that the Moon rotates on its axis at the same average rate that it revolves about the Earth. Thus we always see the *same* hemisphere of the Moon's surface and *never* can see the other hemisphere. To demonstrate this motion, hold a ball or globe rigidly at arm's length and slowly turn around. As the body makes one revolution so does the ball, but only one side can be seen unless the ball is turned in the hands.

In actuality, we have an opportunity to peek around the rim of the Moon to a certain extent, mainly because the Moon revolves in an elliptic orbit. As a consequence of the ellipticity, the rate of revolution is not uniform, although the rate of rotation is nearly so. In addition, the orbit is tipped some 5 degrees to the ecliptic, its pole moving westward around the pole of the ecliptic in about nineteen years. Thus, we can also peek over the poles of the Moon itself by about 5 degrees. These effects that enable us to see some of the Moon's "forbidden" hemisphere are called *librations*. When all of the librations are summed up it is possible for us to see *59 per cent* of the Moon's surface at one time or another, while *41 per cent* can be seen at any time. Only if and when space ships are invented, will man be able to ascertain the character of the remaining 41 per cent of the Moon's surface.

Since the Moon is the nearest celestial object, its distance is the most accurately known. The method of measuring the

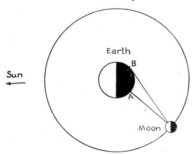

distance is almost exactly that used for Eros, as described in Chapter 4. The nearest that the Moon may approach the Earth's center is some 221,463 miles. An observer, of course, may move some 4000 miles closer than this because he is necessarily located on the surface of the Earth. When one sees the Moon overhead he is closer by about 4000

Fig. 65.—The Moon's distance is less for the observer *A*, who sees the Moon overhead, than for *B* who sees it setting.

miles than at moonrise or moonset (Figure 65). The greatest distance that the Moon can attain is 252,710 miles, while its mean distance is 238,857 miles.

The Earth's atmosphere has a surprising effect upon observations of the rising or setting Moon. Light rays are bent by the atmosphere to such an extent that the *entire Moon** *can*

---

* Or the Sun.

be seen before it has risen and after it has set. The *refraction* of the light coming from empty space into the atmosphere is just about one half a degree, the apparent diameter of the Moon (see Figure 66). Thus, when the Moon's upper limb would be just out of sight were there no atmosphere, the entire Moon is apparently lifted into view. At greater heights the refraction is less and decreases to zero overhead.

Everyone has noticed the strange phenomenon that the Moon appears to be larger when seen near the horizon than

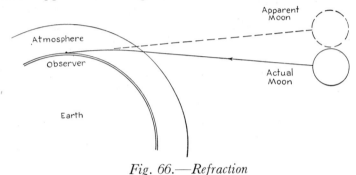

Fig. 66.—Refraction

in the Earth's atmosphere apparently raises the Moon (or Sun) above the horizon after it has geometrically set.

when seen overhead. Actually, when *measured*, the diameter is smaller when near the horizon, because of the small distance effect mentioned above and because refraction flattens the disc slightly. The standard explanation has been that the Moon seems larger when seen in juxtaposition to distant objects on the horizon than when seen against the expanse of the sky. Since the effect is the same for an unbroken horizon at sea as for a land horizon, this explanation is not satisfactory.

Recent studies by Harvard psychologists* show that the effect arises from a peculiar property of the brain and eye.

* Professor E. G. Boring and associates.

When an object is seen directly ahead of the face, with the eyes set squarely in their sockets, it appears larger than when seen at angles above or below. If the observer is lying down, the Moon appears larger when overhead than when near the horizon. The psychologists and physiologists have now the problem of explaining *why* the apparent size of an object depends upon the orientation of the eyes. The astronomer, however, is relieved to have a ready explanation for the often-discussed phenomenon, and to be able to refer the more fundamental problem to other branches of science.

This Moon illusion and the daily changes of the observer's distance from the Moon give rise to the popular paradox that the *Moon appears larger when it is farther away*. The paradox is true during the course of one day, because the rotation of the Earth moves an observer (not too near the poles) farther from the Moon when it is rising or setting; at which times it appears larger because of the illusion. The paradox is not generally true, of course, because the eccentricity of the Moon's orbit changes its distance more during the course of a month than does the Earth's rotation during the course of a day.

Important as the Moon may be as an object for stimulating the human mind, its greatest effect on the Earth results from its power to produce tides. This power is a direct consequence of the inverse square law, by which the nearby Moon attracts the Earth. The cause of the tides was early appreciated by Newton as a confirmation of his law of gravity. Since the attraction is inversely proportional to the square of the distance, the part of the Earth nearest to the Moon is attracted by a force nearly 7 per cent greater than the part farthest away. The force at the center is, of course, the average value, which is exactly sufficient to hold the Moon in its orbit. The 7 per cent differential in force acts on the body of the Earth as a distortion, tending to stretch the globe along the line joining it with the Moon (Figure 67).

A most interesting feature of this tide-raising force is that the face of the Earth *away* from the Moon is distorted in almost exactly the same fashion as the face towards the Moon. One may understand this symmetrical elongation by considering that the lunar hemisphere of the Earth is pulled away from the center, and that the center is pulled away from the opposite hemisphere. When the Earth is stretched along the line joining it to the Moon, the circumference perpendicular to this line is naturally compressed. The net

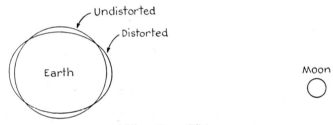

Fig. 67.—Tides.

The Moon elongates the Earth along their line of centers.

tendency of the tide-raising force is to distort the Earth into a shape similar to that of a symmetrical egg. A cross section of the Earth perpendicular to the direction of the Moon would be a circle.

Now if the Earth were absolutely rigid, not yielding to the distorting forces that act on it, all of the tidal effects would occur in the oceans and surface waters. If the Earth were perfectly elastic with no rigidity, the ocean tides would be negligible, although the tidal bulge would still exist. The comparison of ocean tides with the predicted values is exceedingly difficult, however, because the measured tides at shore stations depend upon currents that are set up over the irregular ocean beds. Careful measures of the tides in long pipes show that only 70 per cent of the theoretical effects actually occur. The main body of the Earth yields to the forces to the extent of the remaining 30 per cent. From these measures it is deduced that the Earth as a whole is more rigid than *steel*. The data from observations of earthquakes and from the motion of the Earth's poles confirm this result. Outside the inner (possibly liquid) core the Earth has an average rigidity about twice that of steel.

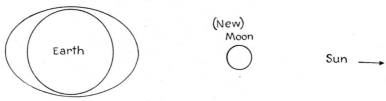

Fig. 68.—Spring tide.

At new moon (or full moon). The Moon and Sun pull together to produce a maximum high tide and a minimum low tide.

A surprising additional result about the Earth was found from the tide experiments. *The Earth is an elastic ball.* Before the experiments, it was generally believed that the Earth was viscous, like thick molasses or glass; if it were distorted a small amount it would probably remain so or else *slowly* regain its original shape because of the small restoring forces. The experiments showed that the entire Earth yields *immediately* to the tide-raising forces, in so far as its rigidity will allow, and that it *immediately* returns to its original shape when they are removed. Thus the Earth is not only more rigid than steel; it is also more elastic.

Although the Moon is the most powerful body in raising tides on the Earth, the Sun also is an important contributor —to the extent of about 30 per cent. The Sun produces tides in exactly the same manner as the Moon. When the two bodies are nearly in line, as at new or full moon, their tidal forces add together (see Figure 68). When their directions are at right angles, as at first or last quarter, their tidal effects tend to cancel (Figure 69). The result is that at new or full moon there are *spring* tides, in which the high tide is very high and the low tide is very low. In between, at first or last quarter, there are *neap* tides, in which the range from high to low tide is reduced to less than half the value at spring tides.

Moon

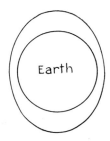

Earth

Sun ⟶

Fig. 69.—Neap tide.

At first or last quarter, when the Sun acts against the Moon. The range in the tides is small. Compare with Figure 68.

Still another factor enters in the production of the tides. When the Moon is nearest to the Earth, at *perigee*, its tide-raising force is greater than when it is farthest away at *apogee*. The range in the lunar part of the tide changes by about 30 per cent because of this change in distance. The combination of the varying amount of the lunar tide, plus the varying summation of the lunar and solar tides, causes large changes in the ranges of the ocean tides.

To see how the tides should occur in practice, we shall first take the ideal case when the actual high tide takes place exactly at the top of each of the tidal bulges shown in Figure 67. In the ideal case there are two high tides each day as the Earth rotates and the observer passes the top of the two bulges. The high tides take place when the Moon is overhead (on the *meridian**) and when it is on the opposite side of the Earth, while low tides occur in between. Because of the revolution of the Moon about the Earth, the tides occur about 50 minutes later each day.

Twice a month, at new moon and full moon, there are spring tides, when the lunar and solar tides add together. In between the spring tides, at first and last quarter, there are the neap tides, when the solar tide subtracts from the lunar tide. Once a year, generally, the new moon occurs at a time when the Moon is near perigee, while about six months later the full moon occurs at this position. The resultant spring tides at these two times of the year are especially high, because of the increased size of the lunar tides. The dates of these maximum spring tides are progressively later by more than a month, from one year to the next, because the direction of perigee is always moving forward around the Moon's orbit, with a period of nearly nine years.

Although the prediction of the theoretical tides is somewhat complicated, the prediction of actual tides at a given station is even more difficult. The theoretical tidal bulge, if the entire Earth yielded to the force, would be about four feet. The actual tides at shore stations generally have ranges of several feet. This discrepancy arises from the fact that the observed tides are measured at the shallow edges of the

---

* The meridian is the line on the sky through the north and south points of the horizon and passing directly overhead.

oceans. As the Earth rotates, the tidal bulges of Figure 67 become, in effect, tidal waves, which pile up on the sloping ocean beds near the shores, much as ocean swells may grow to high waves as they approach a gently sloping beach. In the Bay of Fundy, where this effect is further augmented by the occurrence of a funnel-shaped shore line, the tidal range is often 50 feet or more.

Fig. 70.—Unequal daily tides.
The tide at *A* will exceed that at *B*.

In the open sea, far away from land, the tides must follow the theory very closely, the high tide occurring shortly after the Moon crosses the meridian either above or below. At any point on the shore, however, the time required for the tidal wave to pile up to the maximum height depends entirely upon the contours of the ocean bed. In many places the high tide is consistently late by several hours. This delay is known as the *establishment* of the port, and is used in predicting the tides. If one knows the phase of the Moon and the establishment for his position along the coast, he can easily estimate the times of high and low tides with an error not exceeding an hour. At new or full moon, the establishment represents the number of hours after noon* or mid-

---

* True noon. Use sundial (or even standard time) rather than daylight-saving time.

night that high tide should occur. At first or last quarter the same prediction gives the time of low tide. By adding a correction of 50 minutes for each day elapsed since the nearest preceding phase of the Moon, the times of the tides can be estimated at any intermediate date.

The obliquity of the ecliptic has a marked effect on the tides at stations away from the equator. Because the Earth's poles are tipped from the plane of the Moon's revolution, the two daily tides may differ greatly in range. By reference

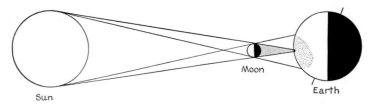

Sun

Moon

Earth

Fig. 71.—Total solar eclipse.

The black shadow is the umbra of total eclipse and the shaded area is the penumbra of partial eclipse. The relative dimensions are much exaggerated.

to Figure 70, one can see that the tide at point (A) will be greater in range than the one at (B), half a day later. At certain stations it often happens that only one high tide instead of two will be appreciable.

Along coastal regions the tides are naturally of great interest and are vital in the everyday affairs of seafaring peoples. For most of the other inhabitants of our globe, the tides are only an interesting phenomenon connected with the sea. In any case the tides are so taken for granted that the Moon's importance is apt to be forgotten. Practically no living person, on the other hand, can fail to be impressed by a second remarkable phenomenon caused by the Moon—a total eclipse of the Sun. At rare intervals because of a striking coincidence, the Moon is placed at just the proper position for its shadow to blot out the Sun's light at any given point on the Earth.

In Figure 71, the Moon's shadow on the Earth is shown. For an observer inside the dark cone (the *umbra*), no direct rays of the Sun are visible; only the *corona*, the outermost vaporous atmosphere of the Sun, can be seen. Outside the umbra, in the partially darkened shadow (the *penumbra*), a part of the Sun's disc is covered. As the Moon's shadow passes over the Earth's surface, the sunlight is slowly dimmed during a period of an hour or more. As the light becomes weaker, with only a thin crescent of the Sun's disc exposed, a phenomenal coolness and silence pervades the atmosphere. The remaining crescent is still so brilliant that it must be viewed through darkened glass. Just before totality the crescent breaks up into a series of beads, as the last rays from the Sun shine through the valleys of the precipitous lunar surface. These *Baily's beads** show brilliantly for a few seconds only. By this time a glowing ring can be seen completely around the Moon, and if, as occasionally happens, one bead alone is bright, the effect is that of a luminescent diamond ring (Figure 72).

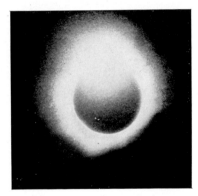

Fig. 72.—Diamond ring.
Eclipse of January 24, 1925, New England. (*Photograph by R. E. Chadbourne.*)

---

* More accurately called Williams' beads, since Samuel Williams observed and described them many years before Francis Baily.

Quickly the sky becomes dark as in the evening dusk. At this moment the corona seems to flare out in all directions about the Sun (Figure 73). Long spikes of light, several Sun diameters in extent, with their bases in the glowing halo of

Fig. 73.—The Sun's corona.

At the eclipse of June 19, 1936, at Ak Bulak, Russia. (*Photograph by the Harvard Observatory.*)

light, point outward into the dark blue of the sky. A few bright stars or planets may be seen. The silence and coolness are awesome and the incandescent silver and blue of the corona are magnificent beyond the expression of words.

In a very short time the spectacle is shattered by the appearance of dazzling rays from the beads that appear on

Fig. 74.—Solar prominence.

Photographs taken ten minutes apart by Frederick Slocum at the Yerkes Observatory. The motions in this short interval cover distances several times the Earth's diameter. The prominences are giant clouds of incandescent hydrogen, calcium and other gases. (*From S. A. Mitchell's "Eclipses of the Sun." Courtesy Columbia University Press.*)

the west limb of the Sun. After totality, the light of the beads appear much brighter and more striking than before totality, because the eye has been accommodated to the semidarkness. Soon the crescent of the Sun brightens the landscape and the partial phase of the eclipse is slowly repeated in reverse order, until the Sun is completely unobscured.

A total eclipse can never continue for much over seven minutes and usually lasts for a considerably shorter time, yet it is a sight that well repays an observer for his effort in travelling to the zone of totality. To the astronomer, it is an opportunity to observe the yet mysterious corona, which is an extended but exceedingly rarified mantle of gas (and dust?) about the main body of the Sun. Also, the *prominences* of the Sun, great whirling or exploding clouds of hydrogen and calcium gases, can be seen (Figure 74), though they can now be well observed without an eclipse. The astronomer has also an opportunity to photograph and measure the

Fig. 75.—Annular eclipse or ring eclipse.

Photograph taken from an airplane. Baily's beads are beginning to form at the right edge. (*Photograph by Major George Goddard, U. S. Army Air Corps.*)

positions of stars near the Sun, where no measures can ordinarily be made because of the brilliancy of the sunlight scattered in the Earth's atmosphere. These measures have shown that the light from distant stars has been minutely deviated by the Sun's mass, in accordance with the predictions of Einstein's theory of relativity. This demonstration, coupled with the anomalous motion of Mercury's perihelion, constitute two of the three astronomical proofs of the relativity theory.

After many months spent in the construction and preparation of instruments, after a long trip to a distant part of the Earth where the eclipse is to occur, and after a strenuous and usually hurried final erection of the instruments at the chosen observing site, the astronomer is indeed happy if he is fortunate enough to have just a few minutes of clear sky at the critical moment. Although solar eclipses are fairly numerous, from two to five each year, such expeditions are

Fig. 76.—Lunar eclipse in infrared light.

Although the Moon is completely within the Earth's shadow it can be photographed in infrared light because of refraction by the Earth's atmosphere. Compare with Figures 77 and 78. (*Photograph by C. D. Shane of the Lick Observatory.*)

necessary because the area of the Earth covered by the dark umbra of totality is very small; the width of the path is only a few miles. In any given location a *total* eclipse can be seen, on the average, only once in 400 years. Sometimes, only the penumbra of the Moon's shadow strikes the Earth, and produces a partial eclipse, while in other eclipses the Moon is so far away that its disc does not completely cover the Sun.

Fig. 77.—Same eclipse in blue light.

Compare with Figure 76. The Earth's atmosphere absorbs more of the blue light than the infrared. One side of the Moon is dark because of clouds on the corresponding side of the Earth. (*Photograph by C. D. Shane of the Lick Observatory.*)

In the latter case the eclipse is *annular* or ring like, the outer ring of the Sun being visible in the center of the path (Figure 75).

Eclipses of the Moon by the Earth's shadow are less numerous than solar eclipses* but each is observable over

---

* In some years none occur, while the maximum number is three. The maximum number of eclipses in one calendar year is seven, five solar and two lunar or four solar and three lunar.

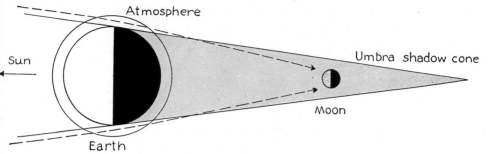

Fig. 78.—The Moon is visible

during a lunar eclipse because the Sun's rays are bent into the umbra by refraction in the Earth's atmosphere.

more than half of the Earth's surface (see Figure 76). Consequently, at a given position on the Earth, a lunar eclipse can be seen quite frequently. A lunar eclipse, however, is not at all spectacular and has little value to the astronomer. When the Moon lies completely in the umbra of the Earth's shadow, it usually acquires a dull copper hue because some sunlight is refracted through the Earth's atmosphere to produce a sunset effect (Figure 78). On rare occasions, the eclipsed Moon is very dark, because the Earth's atmosphere is clouded completely around the twilight zone (compare Figures 76 and 77). In most other respects a lunar eclipse is of little importance and is a matter of only passing interest.

The ancient observations of solar eclipses, on the other hand, have been invaluable in showing that the Moon is tending to increase the length of the day by acting as a brake on the Earth's rate of rotation. The lack of accurate time-keeping devices in antiquity has been no handicap in this type of investigation, because the *place* where a total eclipse of the Sun could be observed is, in itself, a good measure of the time and of the position of the Moon when the eclipse occurred. The Earth must be turned at a certain angle and the Moon must be in a specified position for the Moon's shadow to fall on a given point of the Earth's surface. Calculations based on the records of ancient eclipses show that the day is increasing in length by nearly *one thousandth of a second* every century. This small change almost exactly equals the value predicted to result from the tidal friction.

The energy of the tides is lost in heat because of the friction of the moving water, particularly in the area of the Bering Sea. This energy is taken from the store possessed by the Earth and Moon. The final result is a slowing down of both the Earth's rate of rotation and the Moon's rate of revolution. This theory and its confirmation by eclipse data provide a notable example of joint scientific progress by investigation in four fields—history, geology, physics and astronomy.

The accurate observations of the Moon, Mercury, Venus and the Sun during the last century demonstrate more strikingly irregular variations in the length of the day. For all purposes of astronomy as well as for everyday life, the Earth is the best clock available. If the clock runs fast, the bodies in the solar system will be observed behind their predicted positions. If the clock runs slow, they will be observed ahead. Since the observations of all four bodies, the Moon, Mercury, Venus and the Sun, fit the theory more accurately when a correction in time is made, there is no doubt but that the time is in error. An error in the time means an error in the clock, which is the Earth. In Figure 79 the deviations in the observed positions of Mercury, Venus and the Sun are reduced to the equivalent time error in the position of the Moon. Since the deviation curves are nearly identical* it must be concluded that the Earth is a bad clock. In the latter part of the nineteenth century, the

---

* The observations of the Sun are more difficult and hence the corresponding curve is less accurate than the others.

Earth ran fast by more than a second per year. After 1900 it ran slow by less than a second per year. It has been running fast again since 1920.

A rate of one second per year does not particularly exceed the accuracy of the best pendulum clocks. It is indeed a tremendous rate for the Earth, if we consider the Earth as a rigid body. On the other hand, if the Earth's radius were to expand or contract uniformly by only a few inches, the observed errors could be explained. There is some incon-

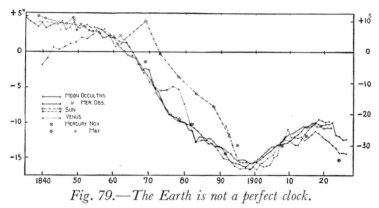

Fig. 79.—The Earth is not a perfect clock.

The above curves, derived by H. Spencer Jones, represent observed errors in the motions of the Moon, Sun, Venus and Mercury. Since, by chance, these bodies could scarcely deviate in the same fashion, the times of observation must be in error. Therefore the Earth turns irregularly.

clusive evidence that the changes in rate are associated with the occurrence of deep earthquakes. Such an association is not surprising in consideration of the fact that some type of alteration must take place in the Earth to cause its rate of rotation to vary.

Thus, from the conclusions of this chapter and the preceding, we see that the Earth is a changing dynamic body, affected by forces from within and from without. How different indeed, is our modern concept of the Earth from that of the ancients!

8

OBSERVING THE MOON

As WE BEGIN THIS SURVEY OF THE MOON'S SURFACE, WE meet the problem that will confront us repeatedly in planetary studies—the problem of observing fine detail by means of a telescope. The telescope is the key of astronomy, an instrument made with the greatest precision and skill with which astronomers can unlock the closed doors of the universe. But even a perfect telescope when used by a most expert observer is limited by an insuperable handicap, the Earth's atmosphere. A short digression from our main topic will clarify our understanding of this fundamental difficulty.

Our knowledge of the surface features of the Moon (Figure 80) or of the planets can be derived only from a study of reflected sunlight, which eventually reaches us after passing the ocean of atmosphere above us. We have seen that refraction in this atmosphere bends the light rays through a small angle; unfortunately, no two parts of the atmosphere refract exactly the same amount. As winds and currents of warm and cool air circulate overhead, each ray of light is bent in a slightly different manner. The result is apparent to the naked eye; the stars twinkle.* A telescope magnifies the

---

* The planets which rarely twinkle because they have finite discs, often can be recognized by their steadiness.

118

Fig. 80.—Moon past first quarter.

Note that the south pole is at the top, as it appears in most astronomical telescopes. (*Photograph by the Lick Observatory.*)

twinkling so much that often the images appear to "boil," as though they were seen across the surface of a hot stove, or across heated desert sands. This boiling turbulence of the atmosphere is called the "seeing," which may be good or bad, the quality depending upon the appearance of stellar images in a telescope.

Besides distorting the images of stars, the atmosphere steals away some thirty per cent of the incoming light and scatters it in all directions. Without an atmosphere our sky would be much blacker at night and equally black in the daytime; thus the stars and planets could be observed by day as well as during the night.* Only a few men have had the opportunity of seeing a black sky during a clear day. In the stratosphere balloon flight of the "Explorer II," Major Albert W. Stevens observed the appearance of the sky as seen at an altitude of 13.7 miles above sea level.

"The horizon itself was a band of white haze. Above it the sky was light blue, and perhaps 20 or 30 degrees from the horizon it was of the blue color we are accustomed to. But at the highest angle that we could see it, the sky became very dark. I would not say that it was completely black; it was rather a black with the merest suspicion of dark blue." "To look directly at the sun through one of the portholes was blinding. The sun's rays were unbelievably intense." †

At a height of 13.7 miles the balloon had surmounted 96 per cent of the mass of the Earth's atmosphere. Completely outside, in the vacuum of space, there would be practically no scattered light, so that the sky would be much darker

---

* On a clear day when Venus is near its brightest light it can be seen by the naked eye—if one stands in a shadow and knows exactly where to look. The brighter stars can also be seen in the daytime if one observes through a tall chimney.

† A. W. Stevens, National Geographic Society, Stratosphere Series no. 2, pp. 195 and 173. Washington, 1936.

than it now appears at night. Against this background, the planets, stars and Milky Way would stand out with a brilliancy unobtainable at the best observing sites on Earth.

The brightness of the night sky affects visual observations only slightly, because the eye is not sufficiently sensitive to be blinded by such weak light. The photographic plate, however, can be exposed until it is blackened by the night-sky light. Our atmosphere, therefore, handicaps tremendously the photography of faint nebulous objects, which may be fainter than the diffuse sky light.

The bad "seeing" sets an unsurmountable barrier to observing fine detail, either visually or photographically, on bright objects such as the Moon and planets. Below a certain angular limit (about a tenth of a second of arc) neither the eye nor the photographic plate can register any detail. For bright objects, the eye is the more effective of the two, because it can register details during those rare instants when the "seeing" is nearly perfect. The photographic plate, on the other hand, requires an appreciable exposure time during which the "seeing" will change.

Hence finer details on the Moon and planets can be seen with a good telescope than can be photographed, although the modern technique of photography has produced marvelous results in registering lunar and planetary features.

To minimize the undesirable atmospheric effects, astronomers have searched to the ends of the Earth to find locations where the "seeing" is exceptionally good. Mountain tops, above the dust and water vapor of lower areas, generally provide very transparent skies, but the "seeing" on a mountain chosen at random may be poorer than at sea level. The Mount Wilson and Lick Observatories, which are responsible for the magnificent photographs of the Moon reproduced in the present chapter, are located on mountain

Fig. 81.—Pic du Midi.

Ascent of the mountain for observations of the Sun. Dr. B. Lyot has, from the Pic du Midi, succeeded in photographing the Sun's corona without an eclipse. (*Photograph Courtesy Société Astronomique de France.*)

tops in California. The Lowell Observatory was established at an altitude of 7000 feet, on the Flagstaff plateau, Arizona, after Percival Lowell had searched "in Japan; in the Maritime Alps, Algeria, Mexico, California and Arizona" for the "best procurable air." Similarly, to obtain improved observing conditions the Southern Station of the Harvard Observatory, (including telescopes, mountings and other equipment) was moved from Arequipa, Peru, to Bloemfontein, South Africa. Likewise, the French astronomers, with complete disregard for human convenience, make the 9400 foot ascent of the Pic du Midi, to secure better observations (see Figure 81). Even when the "seeing" is at its best, the astronomer wishes continually that he could eliminate the atmosphere in order to realize the full capabilities of his optical equipment.

A large telescope will enable an observer to discern finer details than a small telescope—if the "seeing" permits. When the "seeing" is bad, however, the image of a planet or the Moon in a large telescope may be even poorer than in a small one, because of the larger area which allows a greater variation of the air conditions. Hence telescopes of moderate aperature (6 inches to 20 inches) are the most effective for direct visual studies. The great reflectors are used almost exclusively for photographic work, in which their tremendous light-gathering power is of the utmost value. The magnifying power* for any telescope may be chosen at will, by a change of eyepieces. A high power is used when the "seeing" is good and a lower power when it is poor.

The Moon is a spectacular object as seen through any telescope, whether large or small. Galileo was the first man in history to enjoy this privilege and to record his observations for posterity. Even with his small telescope he could detect the mountains, the craters and the great dark areas that make up the features of the "man in the Moon." To him the dark areas looked like great seas of water, hence he called them *maria*, the Latin term for seas (singular *mare*, with the accent always on the first syllable).

In Figure 82, where the Moon is just past full, the maria can be seen to the best advantage. The identifications of a few of them and other conspicuous lunar features are shown in Figure 83. The somewhat whimsical Latin names chosen for the maria cannot be explained on any rational

---

* The magnifying power is the ratio of the focal length of the objective to the focal length of the eyepiece. For a complete description of telescopes and their use see "Telescopes and Accessories" by George Z. Dimitroff and James G. Baker, Harvard Books on Astronomy.

Fig. 82.—Moon nearly full.

See Figure 83 for corresponding map of lunar markings. (*Photograph by the Lick Observatory.*)

basis, although Tranquilitatis, Serenitatis and Frigoris seem appropriate enough. These maria are, of course, not seas but great plains, nearly flat except for the curvature of the surface, and devoid of both air and moisture.

Mare Imbrium (Sea of Showers) and Mare Serenitatis, in the lower center of Figure 82, are very large and nearly circular in shape, in so far as they are clearly outlined. The greatest diameter of Imbrium is over 700 miles, and of Serenitatis, 430 miles. A close-up of a part of Mare Imbrium is shown in Figure 84. The magnificent mountain range outlining the upper left portion of the mare is known as the

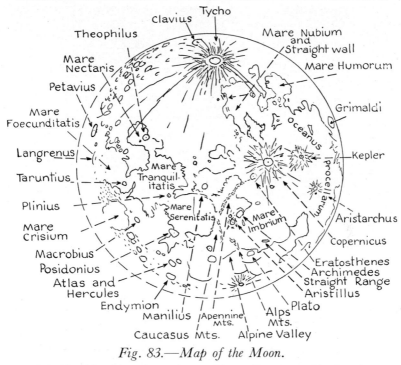

Fig. 83.—Map of the Moon.

With identifications of certain markings. Compare with the photograph, Figure 82. (*Original drawing by Donald A. MacRae.*)

Apennines. These mountains rise some 18,000 feet above the level of the plain, a height that fully justifies the plagiarism in their name. The perspective given by the shadows in Figure 84 reveals that the Apennines are jagged peaks rising sharply from the floor of the mare but sloping away gradually towards the outside. Deep valleys with nearly vertical walls are numerous. The mountain range presents the appearance of models of terrestrial ranges, where valleys have been worn by the erosion of water—but no water exists on the Moon.

Fig. 84.—Mare Imbrium.
Moon at last quarter. (*Photograph by the Mount Wilson Observatory.*)

Paralleling the inner edge of the Apennines can be seen a long somewhat crooked furrow, or *rill*. Several hundred rills have been found on the Moon. They are ditchlike depressions, often a mile deep and extending for as much as 90 miles along the Moon's surface. Since the rills do not show tributaries, as they should if they were formed by erosion, and since their walls are not raised above the surrounding "moonscape," they are most rationally explained as cracks. During cooling it is likely that the Moon's surface would split open in places. Long or deep cracks may also have been filled in or overflowed by subsurface molten material, and show as a different type of marking. Perhaps the long low ridge in the upper center of Figure 84 is actually an extension of the rill system already noted. A great crack that once opened at the base of the Apennines may now show as a rill along a part of its length, as a ridge in another part and, in between, it may have been entirely covered by the flow of molten material.

The more scattered mountains in the lower left of Figure 84 are the Alps. Their most conspicuous feature is the Alpine Valley, a giant cut through the center of the chain. The Valley is 6 miles wide at its broadest portion and 75 miles long, with a level floor. The Valley ends in the midst of the higher regions of the Alps, not far from the mare, thus confounding a theory that the Valley might be a partially filled crack.

The striking appearance of the Mare Imbrium circumference in Figure 84, as compared to the general dullness of Figure 82, is not produced by increased photographic contrast in the first reproduction, nor by an effect of enlargement. In the first view the Moon is full, and the Sun is shining directly down on it; hence we can see no shadows. In the second view the Sun is shining from the right, casting long shadows across our line of sight. Because of the curvature of the Moon, the extreme left edge of Figure 84 is in darkness, except for the high mountain peaks. Along the *terminator*, between darkness and light, the rugged features of the Moon show to the best advantage. The great shadows betray the irregularities that may be invisible when the Sun shines overhead. Because of this effect, the Moon can be best observed when near the first or last quarter. The Sun's rays along the terminator are nearly perpendicular

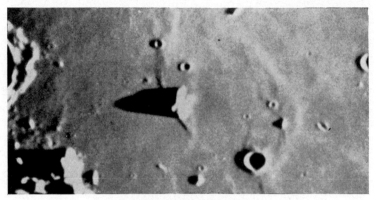

Fig. 85.—Piton.

An isolated lunar peak in Mare Imbrium. Moon at last quarter. (*Section of a photograph by the Lick Observatory.*)

to our line of sight. At the full Moon, we can distinguish only the light and dark areas; the irregularities are lost.

The shadows serve a very useful purpose, in providing an accurate measure of the heights of the lunar features. In Figure 85 the isolated mountain peak, Piton, in the lower left area of Mare Imbrium is even further enlarged to accentuate the shadow. The length of such a shadow can be measured, and the angle of the Sun's rays can be calculated from the phase of the Moon and from the known position of the mountain. Figure 86 illustrates the geometry of solving for the height. The calculations are straightforward, but somewhat involved because of the several angles that must be considered.

Almost everywhere on the Moon there are craters, which become conspicuous when seen near the terminator. The varied character of the craters is apparent in the region of Mare Imbrium, where they stand alone in the open plain.

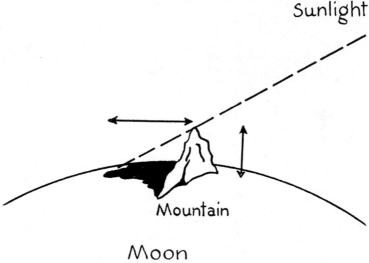

Sunlight

Mountain

Moon

Fig. 86.—Lunar mountain.

The lengths of the shadows cast by lunar markings enable astronomers to measure the heights. Compare with Figure 85.

Some seem smooth and flat within, while others show one or more central peaks, often perforated by smaller craters. Crater walls barely rise above the plain here and there, some of them only partially complete. Close examination reveals that the Moon's surface is covered with an almost unlimited number of small craters (craterlets and crater pits), as though the Moon had been peppered with buckshot.*

---

* The smallest craters visible in the photographs are two or three miles in diameter.

Fig. 87.—Lunar bad lands.

Southern area of the Moon at last quarter. (*Photograph by the Mount Wilson Observatory.*)

The craters can be classified into several types according to their forms. Since fine distinctions can be extended interminably and since the definitions are not always concise or uniform, it is perhaps better not to stress the type names. Many craters possess interior plains as flat as the maria and mountain walls that rise abruptly to define the edges.* The level of the plain may lie above or below the general level outside. The maria too, may be depressed or raised with respect to the average surface level. The largest crater on the Moon, Clavius, is a bulwarked plain, with a maximum diameter of 146 miles from opposing mountain summits. Clavius can be seen near the top center of Figure 87. The curvature of the Moon's surface is sufficient to hide the 20,000 foot mountain walls from an observer standing in the center of the plain.

The crater Tycho, seen slightly above the center of Figure 87, represents a somewhat different type of crater formation.† Only a small fraction of the basin is flat, the crater being more nearly saucer-shaped. The inner slope of the mountain rim is itself ringed, somewhat as though laminated or terraced. These ring-mountain craters are also fairly perfect in form, almost circular, and are rarely encroached upon by lesser craters or other deformations. The ring mountains thus show evidence of having been formed later in the Moon's history than the bulwarked plains, which bear the scars of subsequent tribulations. Other fine examples of the ring mountains are Eratosthenes (Figure 84, upper right-hand corner), and Copernicus (Figures 88 and 89).

The rougher areas of the Moon (Figure 87) are completely covered with a wild hodgepodge of craters within

---

* The Bulwark Plains, bulwarked plains, mountain-walled plains or walled plains.
† Ring mountains or mountain-ringed plains.

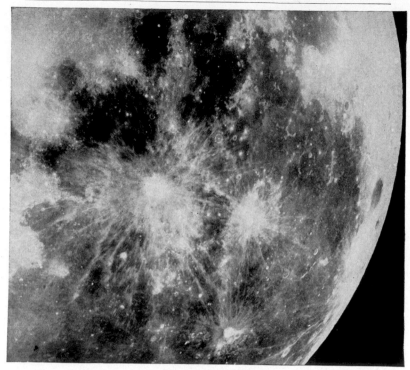

Fig. 88.—Rays.

From the craters Copernicus, left, and Kepler, right. Nearly full Moon. (*Photograph by the Mount Wilson Observatory.*)

craters and craters upon craters. They all appear to have been formed in an entirely "hit or miss" fashion, the newer ones evolving with a complete disregard for all that were there before. Sections of the wall may stand after an old crater has been partly demolished by a new one, and this, in turn, may be pock-marked by smaller craters still more recent.

Across these rugged areas of the Moon and across the extensive plains, are great systems of *rays*, the light-colored streaks that show so conspicuously when the Moon is full,

Fig. 89.—Copernicus.

Moon past last quarter. Compare with Figure 88. (*Photograph by the Mount Wilson Observatory.*)

but almost disappear at the partial phases. A most notable system centers on the crater Tycho (Figure 82) from which the rays can be traced almost around the Moon. In Figure 87 the rays are barely discernible, and Tycho has become just one of many craters, not the most conspicuous of all. The rays cast no shadows and can be detected only by their lighter coloring. They are broken neither by mountains nor by any other features of the lunar topography. Their origin is so far unsatisfactorily explained. It has been suggested that vapors from long invisible cracks may have arisen and condensed, to form the rays, the cracks having been produced in the formation of the craters with which the rays are associated.

Whatever their cause, the rays are a striking lunar feature. Note the complex structures about the craters Copernicus and Kepler in Figure 88. The light color of the rays is shared by the craters with which they are associated, and also distinguishes the rims of a large number of craters. At first glance the region about Copernicus in Figure 88, when the Moon is full, can hardly be identified with the area about Copernicus in Figure 89, at a later phase. The bright crater rims in the latter figure, however, can soon be detected in the former, while some of the larger craters with dull edges have faded to invisibility. A careful comparison of the two photographs is most instructive. The second largest crater in Figure 89, Eratosthenes, can hardly be found in Figure 88, although it is very similar to Copernicus in type.

To the left of Copernicus in Figure 89 are a large number of crater pits, forming a pattern. A lack of exterior shadows indicates that the walls do not rise above the floor of the mare. Such crater pits are very common on the Moon's surface. They are especially noticeable when viewed with a high magnification under good seeing conditions. Exterior

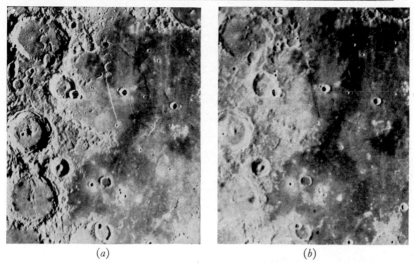

(a)   (b)

Fig. 90.—The Straight Wall.

(a) Moon last quarter, (b) Moon first quarter. (*Sections of photographs by the Mount Wilson and Lick Observatories.*)

shadows cast by their raised walls distinguish the craterlets from the crater pits.

Long serpentine ridges can be seen in the flat plains of Figure 89 and also in Mare Imbrium (back in Figure 84). These low ridges are obviously flow markings, undoubtedly formed when the floors of the maria were in a hot viscous condition. On a flat surface of tar, a horizontal distortion will produce an identical type of marking, especially if the tar is slightly warmed to flatten out the rough ridges.

Another interesting lunar formation is shown in Figure 90, the Straight Wall (or the Railway) some 70 miles in length. The first photograph is a section of Figure 87, below the crater Tycho. The Sun is shining from the right and the Straight Wall shows as a *white* line (to its right, nearly parallel to it is a shorter curved rill). The second photograph was made just after first quarter so that the Sun shines from the left. The Straight Wall now shows as a *dark* line, which proves that the marking is a long straight cliff or wall, elevated 1000 to 2000 feet above the plain and facing towards the right. It is clearly a rock *fault*, where one edge has risen above the other. "Moonquakes," in the dim and distant past, were probably associated with this and other walls visible on the Moon. Similar fault markings, frequent but smaller on the Earth, are the foci of earthquakes.

There are so many interesting formations on the Moon's surface, individual craters with unusual structures, peculiar rills, rays, maria, mountains and cliffs that descriptions could be continued indefinitely. The reader, however, may wish to do some exploring himself, by means of these photographs or with almost any telescope that can be firmly supported. He can soon identify all of the markings described here, and discover many more that are equally interesting. Larger scale charts can be obtained easily by anyone who wishes to learn the proper names of individual lunar formations. Some five thousand markings are officially designated by the International Astronomical Union, and many thousands more have been plotted by assiduous selenographers.

9

THE NATURE OF THE MOON

THE MOON'S SURFACE, AS WE HAVE VIEWED IT IN THE previous chapter is a sublime desolation. The lunar plains are more barren than rocky deserts. The lunar mountains are more rugged than terrestrial peaks above the timber line. Lava beds of extinct volcanoes are more inviting than the lunar craters. Nothing happens on the Moon. Where there is no air there can be no clouds, no rain, no sound. Within a dark lunar cave there would be eternal silence and inaction. A spider web across a dim recess in such a cave would remain perfect and unchanged for a million years.

There can be no colors in the Moon's sky, only blackness and stars during the bitter night two weeks in length and only the glaring Sun during the equally long day. Such a desolate region as the Moon's surface could benefit us only as an observing station for an astronomical expedition, or as a possible source for precious ores, could we cross the 239,000 miles of forbidding vacuum and survive the dangers of open space.

Because the Moon is so close to us, its surface has been studied in minute detail. The magnified image of the Moon as seen in the largest telescopes is equivalent to a naked-eye

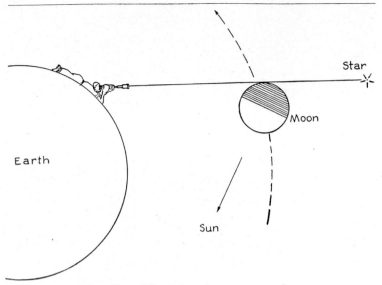

Fig. 91.—The Moon has no atmosphere.

Proved by the instant disappearance of a star when occulted by the dark side of the Moon. There is no fading and no displacement. An atmosphere would produce absorption and refraction. (*Original diagram by Marston Moffatt.*)

view at a distance of less than two hundred miles, near enough for an observer to distinguish objects only a few hundred feet apart. If any changes have occurred in the lunar landscape during the centuries of intensive telescopic observation the changes are too small or uncertain* for the observers to be able to agree upon their reality. No evidence suggests the slightest trace of erosion either by wind or by rain, nor should we expect erosion, because the Moon is observed to retain no atmosphere—at least not more than

---

* Some observers have believed that a small crater, Linné, has shown clouds, and, indeed, has become invisible at times, but the evidence is inconclusive.

one ten thousandth part of the Earth's. If there is any residual trace of atmosphere, it is probably much rarer than is suggested by this approximate upper limit (see Figure 91).

We should suppose the Moon to be devoid of atmosphere because of the smallness of its mass. Its surface gravity is insufficient to prevent the molecules of an atmosphere from being hurled into empty space. Any body, large or small, moving away from the Moon's surface with a speed in excess of one and a half miles per second, would continue to recede indefinitely, completely out of the gravitational control of the Moon. This critical velocity of escape is only slightly greater than the *average* speed of a hydrogen molecule in a gas at ordinary temperatures. Since some of the molecules must always move faster than the average, a hydrogen atmosphere would dissipate from the Moon almost instantly. The dissipation of oxygen or nitrogen would be very much slower because the molecules are heavier than those of hydrogen. In a short time astronomically, however, the Moon would lose any atmosphere it might once acquire, to remain devoid of an atmosphere forever after.

We on the Earth are much more fortunate, because the velocity of escape is much greater, seven and one half miles per second. Even hydrogen will remain almost indefinitely —making it certain that no appreciable fraction of our atmosphere will be lost throughout geologic ages.

Even though there is no weather on the Moon, it is not strictly accurate to say that nothing ever happens there. Day and night alternate over a period of a month, while continuous but light rains of meteors, cosmic rays, electron streams and similar emanations from space keep pelting the lunar surface. In addition, the Earth exerts a considerable gravitational attraction. Among these active forces the two that are probably most important today in altering the Moon's surface are the meteoric impacts and the monthly alternations of temperature. Neither of these factors may produce appreciable changes during a human lifetime, but over hundreds of millions of years they may have been vital agents in molding the Moon's surface layer.

The alternations in temperature from the lunar noon to midnight are extreme, more than 400°F. (see Figure 92), but

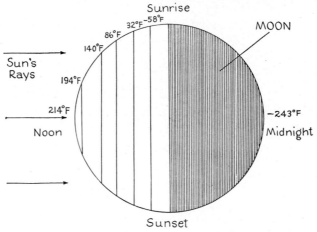

Fig. 92.—Temperatures on the Moon.
(*From measures by E. Pettit and S. B. Nicholson.*)

the alternations take place slowly. Because of the absence of water, the *exfoliation*, or flaking away of rock surfaces by the expansion and contraction, must be very small. Terrestrial rocks exfoliate chiefly because of absorbed moisture that expands on freezing to deteriorate the surface. The very gradual changes in temperature on the Moon allow the rocks sufficient time to adjust their internal temperatures so that exfoliation by pure expansion and contraction is very slow. Over millions of years, however, the exfoliation may be cumulative to such an extent that the lunar mountains may resemble great talus slopes of broken-rock slides. A terrestrial example is shown in Figure 93.

Although the enormous temperature changes from day to night occur very slowly, large changes are observed during an eclipse of the Moon. E. Pettit and S. B. Nicholson, of the Mount Wilson Observatory, measured the Moon's temperature through the course of a lunar eclipse.* It fell from $+160°F.$ to $-110°F.$ in about an hour. Such a quick

Fig. 93.—A talus slope.

Or broken-rock slide. Bases of lunar cliffs and mountains may possess similar slides. (*By W. Cross. From "Geology" by Pirsson and Schuchert. Courtesy John Wiley and Sons.*)

alternation in temperature may be very active in exfoliating the lunar rocks.† The eclipses, therefore, may well be the main factor in the process. If this deduction is valid, a very surprising corollary follows. *The hidden side of the Moon may possess a rougher surface than the observed side,* because lunar eclipses can occur only on the side towards the Earth! This conclusion, unfortunately, is not subject to observational test, and so must remain an interesting possibility.

In discussing the surface molding effects of the meteors we are on a much firmer foundation of knowledge. Meteors

* See Chapter 12, page 194, for method.

† The writer is indebted to Professor Henry Norris Russell for a discussion on this point.

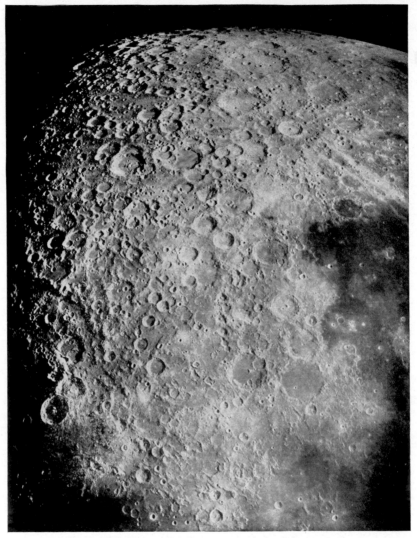

Fig. 94.—Southern area of the Moon.
Moon before last quarter. (*Photograph by the Mount Wilson Observatory.*)

can certainly produce craters, perhaps similar to those that mar the Moon's surface. A fine collection of various sized craters can be seen near the south pole of the Moon, in Figure 94. We know from the previous discussion of the meteor crater in Arizona that giant meteors occasionally fall and create huge craters. Three fundamental questions must be answered, however, before the lunar craters can be accepted as the products of meteoric explosions. Can a meteor result in a crater more than a hundred miles in diameter, with the appearance of the largest lunar craters? If stupendous meteoric masses have collided with the Moon, many more must have struck the Earth. Why do we find no evidence of their craters? Would not volcanic action account satisfactorily for the lunar craters?

The first question cannot be answered positively because of the impossibility of experiments on, or observations of a crater formation encompassing a hundred miles. Small craters produced by artificial explosions simulate the lunar craters in form; the appearance of large craters created by a similar process is conjectural. Figures 95 and 96 compare craters formed by water drops on sand with overly-enlarged lunar craters.

The lack of evidence for gigantic meteor craters on the Earth does not exclude a meteoric origin for the lunar craters. It is reasonable to assume that the large meteoric masses were much more frequent during the early history of the Earth and Moon and that almost all of them have been swept up during past ages. On this assumption, the Earth was once covered with large craters produced by these masses, but geological processes have destroyed the craters and covered up their débris. Only recently-formed craters, such as the one in Arizona, are now identifiable on the Earth, but all are still visible on the Moon. By placing the great meteoric bombardment in the remote past and by

Fig. 95.—Craters in sand.
Produced by drops of water. Compare with Figure 96.

Fig. 96.—Lunar craters.
(*Photograph by the Lick Observatory.*)

avoiding the question whether huge lunar craters could actually be produced in this fashion, we concur with the *planetesimal hypothesis* of the origin of the solar system (see Chapter 14), in which the planets and satellites are assumed to have grown by the accretion of matter when they collided with smaller bodies like the meteors or asteroids.

In keen competition with the meteoric hypothesis for the production of lunar craters, are the arguments for a volcanic origin. Many of the craters simulate the craters of volcanoes on Earth, except for a lack of obvious lava flows near the walls. The large flat plains of the craters and maria, on the other hand, are extremely suggestive of a cooled molten surface. Since the Moon must have been hot when it was formed, volcanoes and large scale flows must undoubtedly have been general over the entire surface. The extensive mountain chains, such as the Apennines, are easily visualized as the edges of gigantic craters, the centers of which were subsequently filled and smoothed by great flows of molten rock.

The Moon at this stage of its development must have been covered with widespread volcanic festers, which slowly cooled and healed to form the maria. The surface areas that cooled somewhat sooner, such as the south polar regions, buckled and warped under the strains of the general contraction. The thin rock skin was covered with volcanoes and lava pools of all sizes. New volcanoes sprang up as the older ones subsided, all in a chaotic melee of smoke, ashes and lava. Craters were formed, weathered by the outpouring gases and ashes, and then undermined by new outbursts.

The small size and surface gravity of the Moon played a considerable role in its evolution. The low surface gravity permitted large scale volcanic activity that would have been curtailed on a more massive body; hence the dimensions of the craters seem not difficult to explain. The small size of the

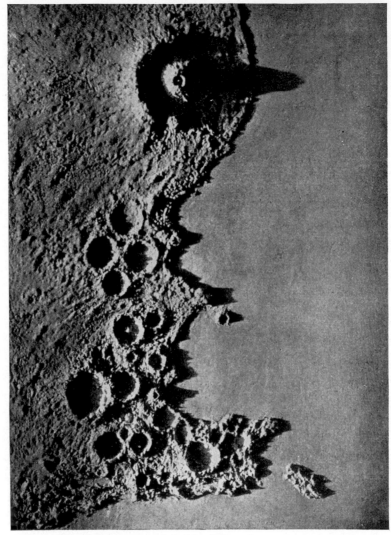

Fig. 97.—Model of Vesuvius crater
and neighborhood of Naples. (*From S. P. Langley's "The New Astronomy." Courtesy Houghton Mifflin Company.*)

Moon accelerated the general cooling, so that the transition period from a completely molten state to a state of relative rigidity was far shorter than for the Earth. By the time the

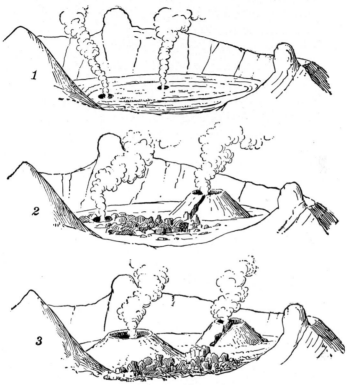

Fig. 98.—Development of Vesuvius craters
during the years 1804 to 1816. (*After W. S. von Waltershausen, "Der Aetna." From R. A. Daly's "Igneous Rocks and the Depths of the Earth." Courtesy McGraw-Hill Book Co.*)

surface of the maria had cooled sufficiently to prevent the rock flows, the Moon had contracted to nearly its present size. The volcanic period was essentially over, except for sporadic outbursts of such craters as Tycho, Copernicus and others of the ray-forming craters.

Logically the rays must have been formed near the end of the volcanic period, or they could not cover the other formations. Earlier rays would have been weathered away by the volcanic débris. It has been suggested that the rays were formed by gases exuded from cracks that the volcanoes produced. The rills are explained as normal cooling cracks, and the straight cliffs as faults.

Such is the story of the Moon's surface features according to the volcanic hypothesis. Qualitative confirmation of such a theory is presented in Figures 97 and 98 where models and drawings of Vesuvius craters are shown for comparison with the previously depicted lunar ones. The general arguments are not entirely changed by an alternative volcanic theory that the craters were formed by the bursting of large gas bubbles from the Moon's interior. This "bubble" theory gains credibility chiefly by the similarity of the Moon's surface to that of boiling mush or porridge.

A long debate upon the question of Meteors vs. Volcanoes, is hardly profitable in the present state of our knowledge. There can be little doubt that *both* processes have been active on the Moon. The question is to determine which was the *dominant* process in crater formation, and in particular, which process produced the large craters. The period of time in which the maria must have cooled seems hardly sufficient for the planets and the Moon to have swept up a large fraction of the meteors. On the other hand, the maria may conceivably have been formed by larger meteoric masses, late in the Moon's evolution. If so, the maria should have produced ray structures. It is very difficult to imagine the maria as having been formed after the interior of the Moon had ceased to be generally molten.

The above argument definitely favors the volcanic process as the predominant one. Meteors, however, may possibly be responsible for the more recent craters—those with ray systems and some of the whiter ones—and for many of the craterlets and crater pits (see Figure 99). Meteors might also

Fig. 99.—Rim of Arizona Meteor Crater.

If on the Moon, this crater would appear as a craterlet or a crater pit. The lunar surface is probably much rougher. (*Photograph by Clyde Fisher.*)

act as trigger mechanisms to start volcanoes. At the stage in the Moon's development when a thin solid crust had formed, a meteor explosion might precipitate a volcano by puncturing or weakening the crust. The volcanic crater might eventually far exceed the dimensions of the original meteoric crater.

The ray structures present an interesting problem of the lunar development. Hardly tenable is the theory of their gaseous origin from cracks. If the craters formed cracks extending nearly around the Moon it is most surprising that none can be observed along any of the rays. An alternate theory that the rays consist of matter violently ejected seems

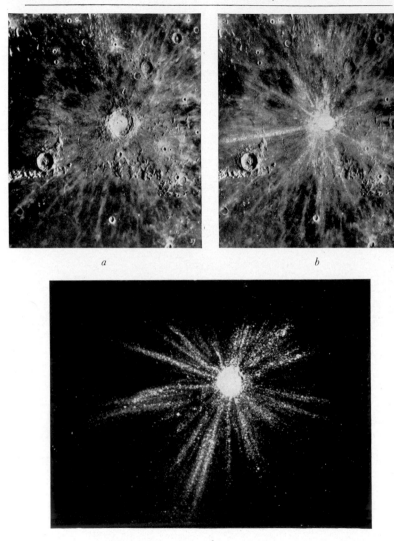

a   *b*

c

Fig. 100.—*Lunar and artificial rays.*

(*a*), Lick Observatory photograph of Copernicus. (*b*), Rays produced on photograph (*a*) by powder explosion. (*c*), Similar rays produced on a black background.

somewhat more likely. Either an explosive volcano or a meteoric impact might produce a ray type of structure. F. E. Wright points out that explosive velocities of less than a mile per second are required to produce lunar rays 1,500 miles in length. A large cannon has a muzzle velocity of only a little over a mile per second and will shoot a projectile for 75 miles on the Earth. Wright calculates that on the Moon the projectile would travel for more than 2000 miles. Volcanoes have been known to eject material at even greater velocities.

A simple experiment will demonstrate, in miniature, the irregular distribution of material thrown out by explosion. A small pile of fine powder, such as flour or talcum powder, is placed on a hard surface, and a large marble or the bowl of a spoon is dropped upon it. The resultant distribution of the powder is very similar in form to the lunar rays. A 14 × 17 inch photograph of Copernicus is rephotographed in Figure 100*a*. Artificial rays were made to emanate from the same crater in *b*. Another set of artificial rays is shown against a black background in *c*. The similarity of the natural and powder systems of rays, is, of course, only a qualitative argument for the explosion theory of ray formation, but is strongly suggestive.

The theory would require that materials of a lighter color exist under the Moon's surface than are visible on the exterior. Since the Moon reflects less efficiently than most of the ordinary volcanic rocks which probably constitute its outer layers, the requirement of the explosion theory seems not too stringent. The surface itself may well be darker than the rocks beneath.

Whether or not meteors have produced the rays and the great lunar craters, there can be no question that small meteoric masses are active in altering the Moon's surface. The Great Meteor Crater in Arizona is barely large enough to be recognized as a crater at the Moon's distance. It would be classed as a small craterlet. Were we able to go to the Moon on a personal tour of inspection, the continuous pitting by much smaller masses should be obvious everywhere. Each meteor produces a miniature explosion as it strikes, throwing rocky and meteoric materials out in all directions. Whether the Moon actually gains mass by these impacts is highly questionable, for quite possibly the explosions are violent enough to eject more material from the Moon than is gained from the meteors. A meteoric particle moving twenty miles per second, upon exploding, might well impart a velocity greater than one and a half miles per second* to more than its own mass of material. Since there is no atmosphere to resist the loss, such material would leave the Moon forever. In any case the quantity of matter involved is trivial. At the present rate of meteor falls, a layer less than an inch thick would be accumulated in 3,000,000,000 years, if no material were lost by the impacts.

One effect of the meteoric impacts is irrefragable: the Moon's surface must be covered with a layer of coarse dust. Each explosion must distribute lunar and meteoric material, probably more of the former, as fragments and solidified droplets over a considerable area around the point of impact. Since volcanic action would also produce a similar result the observations must provide evidence for dust on the Moon's surface or else we must discard all of our theories. Fortunately for the theories, there is abundant evidence favoring the dust layer. Most striking and conclusive are the observations, mentioned above, made during a lunar eclipse. In the course of only an hour the surface temperature dropped from $+160°F.$ to less than $-110°F.$ No solid granite rock, or similar solid that is a fairly good heat con-

---

* The above-mentioned velocity of escape.

ductor, could cool so rapidly after having been heated for several days. Only insulating materials can respond so readily to external changes in temperature.

The Moon's surface, therefore, is covered with some insulating material, pulverized rock, dust or some porous material such as pumice or volcanic ash. Again, however, we are unable to distinguish between the volcanic and the meteoric theories. Both theories predict the observed conditions.

Additional evidence favors the occurrence of very small craters (or depressions in a pumicelike rock), much too small ever to be resolved individually by direct observation. The manner in which sunlight is reflected at various angles indicates that the smoothest appearing areas of the lunar surface are completely covered with small cuplike depressions. We can easily visualize the ashy surface honeycombed with these tiny craters, each new meteor adding a small pit to those already present. As motley an assortment of craters must exist in miniature as we can observe on a grand scale in photographs. Even the dust-free sides of precipitous rocks must be covered with meteoric scars. Nowhere on the Moon is it likely that one could find a smooth area, except possibly at the base of a steep rocky slope where dust and rock débris had formed in a heap; furthermore, the surface must be so webbed with deep crevasses and fissures that it would be impassable.

Since the Moon is a poor reflector (its *albedo* or reflecting power is about seven per cent), and since its reflected light is yellowish or reddish as compared to the original sunlight, the surface generally simulates the appearance of dark brown rocks. The dust must be coarse in structure, possibly like gravel, because fine dust is usually an excellent reflector. The surface rocks are probably pumicelike in character, full of small bubbles produced as the subsurface gases carried the molten materials upwards. The low atmospheric pressure (or none at all) would accentuate the formation of these small bubbles in the rocks.

Had the Earth been unable to retain an atmosphere, its surface would probably be similar to that of the Moon, indescribably rough and barren. Air and water, however, have made possible the surface that we know, and have led to the evolution of living forms.

Rugged as the Moon appears, the extremes of height and depth are less than those on the Earth. The highest lunar mountain rises 25,000 feet above the average level, slightly less than the height of Mt. Everest above sea level. The deepest crater floor is depressed some 24,000 feet, less than the 35,400 feet of our greatest ocean deep.*

If both the Earth and Moon cooled from molten masses, the interior of the Moon, as discussed above, reached equilibrium and stability far more quickly than the Earth. Thus the wrinkling of the outer skin was less than the Earth's, in which the great internal mass is still flowing, to produce earthquakes and external warping. The lack of water and consequent erosion on the Moon completely alters its "geological" problems.

That the Moon is now permanently moulded, subject only to exceedingly minor alterations, is evidenced by the fact that it rotates with the same face to the Earth. Our satellite is "frozen" with a tidal bulge elongated along our line of sight.† The tide-raising forces of the Earth have already completed their work by permanently distorting the Moon's shape. Only exceedingly small variations in this distortion now persist, when the librations, caused by the Moon's elliptic motion, permit the tidal forces to act at

---

* Off the island of Mindanao, in the Philippine Group.
† An elongation of some 3000 feet.

small angles to the permanent bulge. The Moon is probably so stable now, in its old age, that even "moonquakes" are extraordinarily rare if, indeed, they can occur at all.

Bidding farewell to the Moon, Goddess of the Night, we may perhaps carry with us the pensive melancholy of disillusionment. The cold and penetrating light of science discloses that the silvery Goddess, notwithstanding her pale nocturnal charm, is in fact ancient, wrinkled and taciturn. The story of her youth, if we could only discover it, would undoubtedly be an exciting page of history.

10

JUPITER, THE DOMINATING PLANET

FROM THE BARREN, INFLEXIBLE FEATURES OF THE MOON, we now turn our attention to the antithesis of everything lunar, to the colossus of planets, Jupiter, whose surface presents a turmoil of never ceasing transmutations. We find this planet some four hundred million miles away in space; its mass amounts to more than three hundred Earths, while its volume exceeds that of our planet by more than a thousandfold. Through the telescope we can see Jupiter as a golden disc with dark and light bands roughly parallel to each other. Reddish or brown shades of color catch our eyes while we note the irregular cloudlike patches that break the uniformity of the bands (Figure 101a). The disc seems slightly elongated in the direction of the bands, and careful measures confirm our judgment; this diameter is greater than its normal by one part in fifteen.

Within an hour's observation the planet appears to have turned slightly; in only 9 h. 55 m. it will have made a complete revolution. On a succeeding night we find that the bands and surface markings are much the same as before,

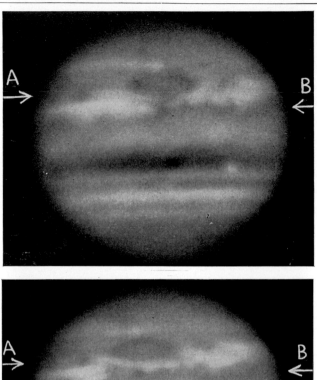

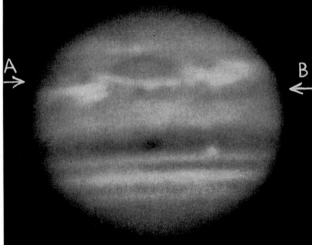

Fig. 101 a and b.—Jupiter in 1928.

The photographs, taken $49\frac{1}{2}$ hours apart show changes in the Great Red Spot and motions of clouds near it. Note spots indicated by arrows. (*Photograph by E. C. Slipher of the Lowell Observatory.*)

but that the details are slightly changed (compare Figures 101*a* and *b*). Within a few weeks the band structure is considerably transformed though the general character of the markings remains unaltered. Since the axis of rotation is perpendicular to the plane of the slowly changing bands, the bands must result from great "trade winds" or atmospheric currents parallel to the equator. The atmosphere must be deep, so that the rapid rotation can preserve these currents, perhaps in some fashion similar to the maintenance of the trade winds in our own atmosphere.

The rotation of Jupiter is indeed rapid, so rapid that the equator turns with a velocity of about 25,000 miles per hour. The consequent centrifugal force of rotation is sufficient, even when acting against 2.6 times the surface gravity on Earth, to flatten the sphere by the appreciable amount that we have already noted. The amount of this flattening, however, is not as great as would be expected were the interior of Jupiter similar to the interior of the Earth. Involved calculations show that the ratio of the density near the center of Jupiter to the density of the upper levels must be greater than for the Earth. Thus the rate of increase in density from the surface to the center is relatively more rapid for Jupiter.

This peculiar density distribution in Jupiter acquires a striking significance when we recall that the mean density of the entire planet is only one and one third times that of water. The high concentration of material towards the center requires that the outer layers be much less dense than water. Since there are few solids or liquids so rare, we must conclude that the outer layers of Jupiter are gaseous or are composed of exceedingly light materials.

The existence of a very deep atmosphere is evidenced by certain of the directly observed markings. Most startling of all the features on the Jovian surface has been the Great Red

Spot, first noted in 1878. It appeared as a brick-red area, elongated some 30,000 miles in a direction parallel to the equator. It is still observable, as an oval spot of varying color and character, but has never been as conspicuous as during the first few years after discovery. Figure 102 presents the

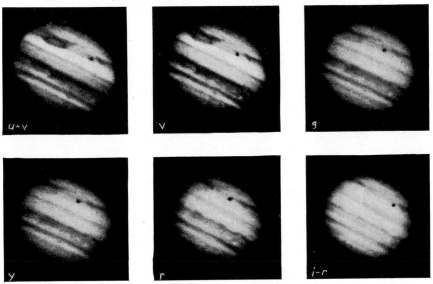

Fig. 102.—Jupiter photographed in six colors.

u-v = ultraviolet, v = violet, g = green, y = yellow, r = red, i-r = infrared. The black dot is the shadow of a satellite. (*Photograph by W. H. Wright, of the Lick Observatory.*)

aspect of Jupiter and the Red Spot as photographed in six different colors. In the ultraviolet and violet light the Spot is dark against the planet's disc. In green and yellow light it is just visible, and in the red and infrared the Spot has disappeared. A white object would show equally well in all colors, while a red one lacks the violet, blue and green colors; hence it appears dark when photographed in these colors. The impartial "eye" of the photographic plate therefore verifies the color of the Great Red Spot. The general reddish tinge of other markings is also evidenced by Figure 102.

The Great Red Spot does not rotate uniformly with the planet but drifts about considerably; it once wandered away from its mean position by nearly a quarter of Jupiter's circumference. Such freedom of motion shows unquestionably that the Spot is a floating disturbance. Other such semipermanent markings are observed on Jupiter's surface, and all wander about to some extent—proof that the Jovian atmosphere is deep and complex.

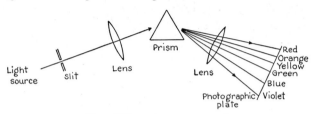

Fig. 103.—A spectrograph.

Schematic drawing. The optical functions of the lens are not indicated.

We know two of the chemical constituents of this atmosphere; they are the gases ammonia and methane (or marsh gas). How we can determine the chemical composition of a gas four hundred million miles away is indeed a feat of scientific magic. It is done with a spectrograph, an instrument that separates light into its fundamental colors and photographs the entire sequence, from the ultraviolet through the blue, green, yellow, red and infrared. The light to be analysed first passes through the entrance slit of the spectrograph (Figure 103), then through a lens to a prism, the heart of the instrument. The prism disperses the light into its constituent colors or spectrum. The spectrum is identical in character to a rainbow except that the colors are much better separated. A second lens of the spectrograph serves to focus the spectrum on the photographic plate where a permanent record is made. With a long exposure the photographic emulsion registers light much too faint to be seen with the naked eye.

The spectrograph solves a number of our difficult problems, one of the most important being the identification of chemicals in a gaseous mixture. The light that escapes from a luminous or absorbing gas reveals the character of the gas. Each atom or molecule is a vibrating pulsing entity; the vibrations are those of the elementary negatively-charged particles, the electrons, which are held in miniature orbits about the heavier positively-charged nuclei of the atoms. Two or more atoms in a molecule also rotate and vibrate around each other, while the electrons in the atoms spin about in their complex gyrations.

All of these motions and vibrations in atoms and molecules represent discrete amounts of energy, exceedingly minute but characteristic for each kind of atom or molecule. When an atom loses energy by a change in rate of vibration, the energy is radiated into space as a photon* of light, with a definite amount of energy, a certain color and a certain wavelength of vibration. These waves of light belong to the same family as radio waves but are much shorter. The waves of red light are about twenty-five millionths of an inch long, while those of blue-green light have a length of only twenty millionths. Infrared or heat waves may be several times longer; ultraviolet light waves are shorter.

The compressed incandescent gas near the surface of the Sun sends out all colors and therefore all wavelengths of light. When such continuous light traverses a layer of cool gas, such as our atmosphere or the atmosphere of Jupiter, the vibrating atoms and molecules are activated, and steal

---

* A photon is the smallest element of radiant energy. It behaves at times like a particle but usually like a wave.

from the beam precisely those wavelengths characteristic of their rates of vibration. When we analyse the light with a spectrograph we measure the wavelengths that are missing, and so identify the atomic or molecular thieves who are responsible for the loss. The missing wavelengths appear as dark *lines* in a spectrum.

In Jupiter's atmosphere the molecules of ammonia and methane are responsible for the huge losses shown by the spectra of Figure 104. (Other dark lines to be seen in these

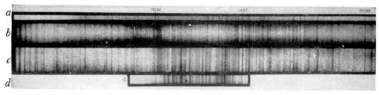

Fig. 104.—Spectra.

(*a*) Sun, (*b*) Saturn, (*c*) Jupiter, (*d*) ammonia gas. Infrared light. Note identity of the absorption lines for Jupiter and ammonia, the weakness for Saturn and absence for the Sun. (*Spectra by Theodore Dunham, Mount Wilson Observatory.*)

spectra have been produced by the gases of the Sun's outer layer and by the Earth's atmosphere.) Theodore Dunham of the Mount Wilson Observatory was able to identify these two gases by separately compressing them in a sixty-foot pipe. He discovered that the wavelengths lost from a light beam reflected twice through the pipe agreed identically with the wavelengths absent in the spectrum of Jupiter. Some thirty feet of ammonia gas at a standard atmospheric pressure are equivalent to the amount in Jupiter's atmosphere, to the depth that sunlight penetrates before it is reflected back to us. For methane, the corresponding amount is one half a mile.

Now the presence of these particular gases tells us immediately that hydrogen is very abundant in Jupiter's atmosphere. Ammonia (NH_3) is composed of one nitrogen atom to three of hydrogen, while methane (CH_4) contains one carbon atom to four of hydrogen. We may conclude that hydrogen is so abundant that it combines with all the carbon and nitrogen present. Probably it has also combined with the available oxygen to form water (H_2O), but the water has frozen and sunk to the bottom of the atmosphere, out of our sight. If so, there may well be a thick layer of ice somewhere far beneath the clouds on Jupiter. Free hydrogen gas probably constitutes the major part of the atmosphere, but is undetectable with the spectrograph; hydrogen gas, when cool, absorbs light only in the extreme ultraviolet, where our atmospheric shield is completely effective.

A great abundance of hydrogen in Jupiter confirms our previous conclusions about the low density of the outer layers and about the rather low density of the entire planet. Because hydrogen is the lightest element possible, we now understand how the material of Jupiter can be so rare. A schematic model of Jupiter's internal constitution has been deduced by Rupert Wildt of Princeton University. The outer layers, for the first 18 per cent of the radius, consist chiefly of compressed hydrogen; an ice layer fills the next 39 per cent and a metallic rocky core constitutes the remaining 43 per cent (see Figure 105). The ice would be compressed by the enormous pressures to a density of 1.5 that of water, hydrogen to 0.35, while the core is assumed to have a density of 6.0. Although we may never be able to demonstrate the detailed veracity of this model, it provides a reasonable representation of conditions beneath the cloud-filled atmosphere.

The composition of the great clouds is no longer a matter of pure speculation. The known abundance of ammonia and methane, combined with a knowledge of the temperature at

Jupiter's surface, provide sufficient clews to reveal the secret. The surface temperature is about $-216°F.$, approximately the temperature we should expect if the surface is heated solely by the Sun. Ammonia boils at $-28°F.$ and freezes at $-108°F.$, while methane boils at $-259°F.$ and freezes at about $-300°F.$ Hence ammonia* on Jupiter is frozen, while the methane is gaseous. The clouds, consequently, must

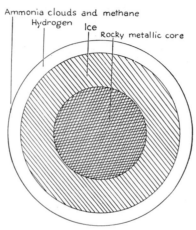

Fig. 105.—Jupiter's internal structure according to R. Wildt.

consist of small ammonia crystals suspended in the atmosphere, as ice crystals are held in terrestrial clouds. The ammonia vapor that we observe has *sublimed*† from the solid crystals, otherwise no ammonia gas should be detected.

The strong coloring of some of the clouds has been remarked earlier in this chapter. The photographs of Figure 106 portray distinct variations in shades and tints over the several belts and clouded areas. The equatorial band is dark

---

* Household ammonia consists of the gas dissolved in water.
† Evaporated from the solid state. Ice sublimes rapidly at temperatures much below freezing.

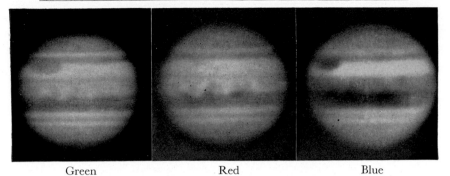

| Green | Red | Blue |

Fig. 106.—Colors on Jupiter.

Photographs taken in the green, red and blue. Note the darkness of the Great Red Spot in the blue light. (*Photographs by E. C. Slipher of the Lowell Observatory.*)

in blue light, but unnoticeable in the green and red. It is therefore yellow in color, since red and green light combine to produce the optical sensation of yellow. A careful comparison of these excellent photographs will disclose a wide range of hues in addition to the brick-red of the Great Red Spot. Wildt has suggested that the clouds are contaminated with traces of metallic compounds, particularly those of sodium, to discolor the otherwise white crystal reflections.

The region of Jupiter most difficult to visualize is perhaps the upper transition layer between the clouded atmosphere and the solids (?) beneath. The gravitational force on the upper gases produces a rapid increase of pressure at greater depths in the atmosphere, and introduces the difficult problem of calculating the level at which the gases and clouds will form a solid substratum. A gas, such as methane, may remain vaporous even after being compressed far above its usual solid density, if the temperature increases with the depth—as is quite likely on Jupiter. The observed temperature of the planet, in agreement with expectations, shows only that Jupiter does not radiate *much* heat; even so, the lower levels may be considerably warmer than the upper. It is quite possible that no distinct solid surface exists, that at some distance below the clouds the gases become very dense until a thick slushy layer (perhaps solid ammonia particles) begins. The slush becomes heavier with depth until it is effectively solid.

The continued existence (over a hundred years*) of the Great Red Spot and other semipermanent markings adds another complexity to the problem of whether Jupiter may have a solid surface. The South Tropical Disturbance, less conspicuous than the Red Spot, moves somewhat irregularly around Jupiter's equator in about two years. It approaches the Red Spot with a speed of several miles per hour, hastens to catch up with the Spot, then seems to pull the Spot along for some distance. After the encounter the Spot drifts back while the Disturbance continues on its way. Such motions preclude the possibility that a continuous volcanic action is responsible for the South Tropical Disturbance, or even for the Red Spot.

Relative motions of a similar type are apparent in the photographs of Figure 107. A small white spot, just north of (below) Jupiter's equator, advances upon the dark spot slightly south and to the east of it (up and to the left). The gain is appreciable in the three weeks between the first and second photographs. Figure 101, earlier in this chapter, depicts relative motions of 8000 miles per day between the Great Red Spot and darker spots near it. The small interval between the exposures and the less conspicuous character of the small spots render the motions more difficult to detect in the reproductions.

---

* After the Red Spot became conspicuous it was possible to identify its presence on drawings as early as 1831.

Fig. 107.—Rapid changes on Jupiter.

These photographs were taken on Sept. 14, Oct. 6 and Nov. 30, respectively from left to right (1928). Note relative motion of the small white spot just below the equator. (*Photographs by E. C. Slipher of the Lowell Observatory.*)

Although the semipermanent markings cannot be continuously maintained by volcanic action, their colorations by metallic contaminations is highly suggestive of an eruptive origin. Since we can find no obvious alternative to the volcanic hypothesis, why should we not investigate to find whether it can be reconciled with the observations? Are lifetimes of forty years for the South Tropical Disturbance or a hundred years for the Great Red Spot so enormously long? The least diameters of the clouds are comparable with the Earth's diameter, while the clouds extend parallel to Jupiter's equator for much greater distances. Although we cannot postulate that they are as deep as their breadths, they may possibly extend to depths of five hundred miles. At greater depths the pressures (perhaps a hundred thousand atmospheres) would compress the gases to a quasi-liquid or -solid, depending upon the temperature. If we imagine the clouds to have been originally formed out of huge volcanic bubbles or eruptions from Jupiter's deep interior, the out-

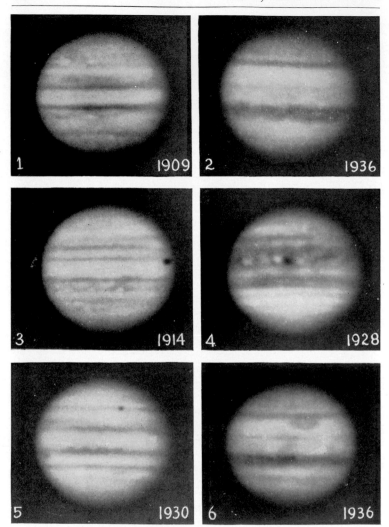

Fig. 108.—Long time-changes on Jupiter.

Photographs were taken in the years indicated. Shadows of the satellites appear on the 1914 and 1930 photographs. (*Photographs by E. C. Slipher of the Lowell Observatory.*)

bursting material might well discolor a volume of material comparable to the Moon. We can hardly be surprised that such a gigantic cloud-blotch preserved its identity for a number of years. Its life might well be increased if its composition were appreciably different from the rest of the atmosphere, hotter or colder for example, or lighter in density. A nucleus of metallic materials might remain intact and continue to stain the surrounding clouds for many years.

The unusual motions of the markings, however, arouse one's suspicions concerning the existence of any solid layer within a great distance of Jupiter's surface. One is reminded of the peculiar rotation of the entirely gaseous Sun, the equatorial regions rotating more rapidly than the polar regions. On the average no such anomaly appears in Jupiter's rotation. Nevertheless, the great irregularities in motion might well be damped out by frictional drag were an actual surface present. *

The activity of the general cloud-forming agencies on Jupiter is admirably clear in the series of photographs in Figure 108. The surface features at the several epochs are completely varied. The subsurface structure of this planet can scarcely be stable when such marked transformations are manifest on the exterior.

JUPITER'S SATELLITES

Jupiter's family of satellites is the most numerous in our system and could easily provide material for a lifetime of study. All the dynamic problems of the entire solar system are here reproduced on a miniature scale (Figure 109). Of the eleven satellites so far discovered, the four largest † out-

---

* The trade winds on the Earth are maintained by the temperature variations with latitude and time, and by the evaporation of ocean water.
† They would be just visible to the naked eye if they could be observed away from Jupiter's overpowering brilliancy.

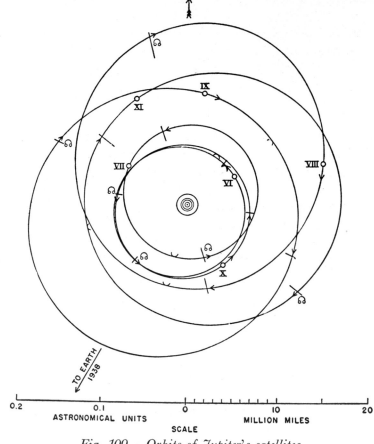

Fig. 109.—*Orbits of Jupiter's satellites.*

The four Galilean satellites and Satellite I occupy the small central orbits. Arrows indicate direction of motion. Arcs of small circles represent the intersections of the orbit planes with the ecliptic. The actual orbits do not intersect because of their various inclinations. (*Diagram by S. B. Nicholson. Courtesy the Astronomical Society of the Pacific.*)

shine the next in size by a thousandfold, and the faintest one by a factor of a hundred thousand. Galileo discovered the four satellites in January 1610, very shortly after he had

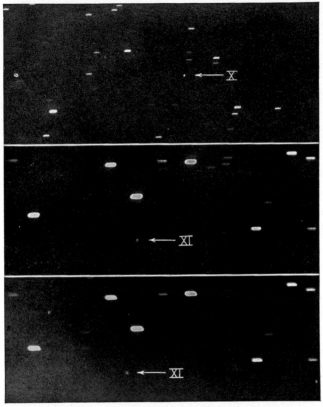

Fig. 110.—Jupiter's satellites X and XI.

Photographed by S. B. Nicholson, their discoverer. (*Photograph by the Mount Wilson Observatory.*)

constructed his first telescope: they are therefore called the Galilean satellites. They move in small orbits ranging from about one to five times the Moon's orbit in size. Because of the enormous mass of Jupiter, however, the periods of revolution are much shorter, from about one to sixteen days. Of the fainter satellites, the fifth, discovered by Barnard in 1892, revolves with a period just under a day while all the others have longer periods; the greatest is more than two years.

The faintest satellites (IX, X and XI) can be photographed only by the larger telescopes, and were all discovered by Seth B. Nicholson, now of the Mount Wilson Observatory. Two appear as barely distinguishable white dots in Figure 110. Since the satellites move in the sky and since long exposures are necessary, the telescope is made to follow the satellites and thus produces trailed star images.

The eighth, ninth and eleventh satellites are of particular interest because they move in retrograde orbits, opposite in sense to the motions of all other bodies (except comets) inside Jupiter's orbit. Jupiter itself rotates in the plane of its orbit, which is practically identical with the plane of the Earth's orbit. This contrariness on the part of the three satellites provides some material for speculation. Someone has suggested that they were once asteroids which, by chance, happened into precisely the proper positions near Jupiter to be captured by the gravitational attraction of this great planet. The theoretical stability of the present orbits is some measure of the chance of such a capture. It is true that the eighth satellite (direct motion) moves so far from Jupiter that at times its situation is very precarious because of the solar attraction, but it also appears that the retrograde motion of the other three is a safeguard from loss to the Jovian system. The best theory and opinion make the asteroid origin rather improbable.

Three of the Galilean satellites are similar to the Moon in size, mass and density; they must, like the Moon, be constructed largely of rock. The third satellite, Ganymede, is only 0.6 as dense as water. It may consist of the same substance as the outer layers of Jupiter, perhaps of hydrogen combined in ammonia and water—both frozen. In one respect these satellites all differ from the Moon, they are excellent reflectors of sunlight. Their surfaces, therefore, must be entirely different in character from that of the Moon, perhaps covered with frozen gases that would long since have evaporated and escaped had they ever been present on the Moon. Little is known about the fainter satellites except that they are very small, the outermost ones being only a few miles in diameter.

The Galilean satellites have made possible one major contribution to physical knowledge. When Olans Roemer* observed the eclipses of these satellites by Jupiter, he discovered that the time intervals between the eclipses were greater when the Earth was receding from Jupiter than when it was approaching. In 1675 he came to the conclusion that the apparent variations in the periods were caused by the *finite* velocity of light; previously light had been suspected of moving instantaneously. When the Earth is receding from Jupiter the light must travel a successively longer path between eclipses, while in approach the path is successively shortened.

In this manner Jupiter and its satellites have made a major contribution to our physical knowledge, in addition to their intrinsic contribution to astronomical knowledge.

---

* A Danish astronomer who invented several of the most important instruments of positional astronomy. His great contributions, unfortunately, were little appreciated during his lifetime.

11

THE OTHER GIANTS—SATURN, URANUS AND NEPTUNE

SATURN

AMONG THE INNUMERABLE CELESTIAL OBJECTS THAT MAY be seen through a telescope, the most beautiful of all is perhaps the planet Saturn. When viewed in the evening twilight while the sky is still bright, the yellow gold ball and its unbelievable rings shimmer in a brilliant blue medium, more like a rare work of art than a natural phenomenon. Lightly shaded surface bands, more uniform than those of Jupiter, parallel the great rings; only occasionally can one distinguish detailed markings that will reveal the rapid turning of the great globe. The central brilliance fades away towards the hazy limb of the planet's disc, and the rings at their borders appear to dissolve into the sky.

Where Saturn's rings cross the disc a hazy dark band outlines their innermost edge (Figure 111a). This crape ring is most readily discerned by its faint shadow on the planet's disc. The outer rings also cast shadows on Saturn, which in turn, completely eclipses large sections of the rings. The polar regions of the planet, perpendicular to the plane of the rings, are darker than the other edges of the disc, and, when seen under good observing conditions, present a slightly greenish appearance. Three major bright divisions of the rings are easily detected, the brilliant middle ring (B), the fainter outer ring (A) and the barely luminous crape ring or inner ring. The two outer rings are broken by narrow dark

a   *b*

Fig. 111.—Saturn's rings disappear when seen edge on.

(*a*) The rings are near their maximum opening. (*b*) The rings are edge on. See Figure 112. (*Photographs by E. C. Slipher, Lowell Observatory.*)

divisions, similar to Cassini's division* that separates rings A and B; these fine markings are detectable only under ideal observing conditions (drawn in Figure 27, Chapter 3). No observer has ever succeeded in distinguishing the slightest irregularity or discontinuity around the ring surfaces except for the dark divisions concentric with the planet.

Saturn's rings lie precisely in the plane of the equator, which is inclined some twenty-eight degrees to the plane of the Earth's orbit. Since the plane of the rings remains fixed

---

* Named for its discoverer, the first director of the Paris Observatory. He described the rings in 1675.

as Saturn moves around the Sun we can see the rings from above (north), from below (south), and twice edge on, during one revolution (Figure 112). When the rings are tipped at the greatest angle for terrestrial observation they reflect nearly twice as much sunlight as Saturn itself, but when the rings are edge on they completely disappear for a day or two (Figure 111*b*). The thickness of the rings is therefore

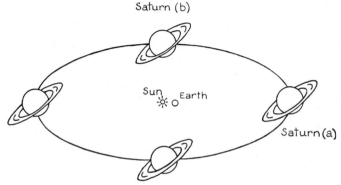

Fig. 112.—Changing views of Saturn's rings.

As seen from the Earth. Positions (*a*) and (*b*) correspond respectively to the views (*a*) and (*b*) of Figure 111.

exceedingly small, perhaps even less than ten miles. Nowhere else in the universe do we know of a natural surface as flat and relatively as thin as the ensemble of Saturn's rings. A single sheet of the paper in this book is comparatively ten times as thick as the rings, and is far from plane. The greatest diameter of ring A is some 170,000 miles. The ratio of thickness to diameter is $10/170,000$. The page is some eight inches long, so that the paper proportionately should be about $1/2000$ inches thick—its actual thickness is roughly $1/200$ inches.

We know that these rings are composed of individual fragments of matter, each moving in its own orbit about Saturn according to Newton's law of gravitation. The irrefutable demonstration of this fact is an excellent example of scientific progress by the alliance of a physical theory with a special observing technique. The instrument used is again the spectrograph; the physical theory includes the laws of physical optics and of gravitation; the demonstration proves that any zone in the rings moves at precisely the speed that would be expected, were it composed of particles moving in circular orbits.

We have seen in the preceding chapter how the spectrograph can be used for identifying a gas by the spectral lines, or wavelengths, subtracted from the light when it passes through the gas. If the gas is approaching us, or we are approaching the gas, more of the waves enter the slit of our spectrograph in a given time interval than though we were relatively at rest. The waves appear to be closer together because of the relative approach, with the result that all the wavelengths are measured shorter than before. Wavelength decreases towards the violet end of the spectrum; thus all the dark lines of missing wavelengths are shifted towards the violet. The amount of the shift is proportional to the velocity of approach divided by the velocity of light. *
When we are receding from the source of light the waves are apparently spaced farther apart, their lengths are greater and the dark lines are displaced toward the red end of the spectrum.

Careful measures of the wavelengths of the lines in the Sun's spectrum can be made on direct spectra of the Sun †
and also when the sunlight has been reflected from a planet, satellite or other object in the solar system. The shifts in wavelength are then a measure of the sum of the object's

---

* The phenomenon described is known as the Doppler-Fizeau effect. In sound the analogous Doppler effect is exhibited by the drop in pitch of the bell of a train as it passes.

† With a small correction for the known velocity of the Earth.

velocities with respect to the Sun and with respect to the Earth. The reflection naturally introduces the effect of the object's motion relative to the Sun, a shift in wavelength which is already present when the light reaches the object, and adds to it the effect of the motion with respect to the Earth. When the reflected sunlight from Saturn's rings is focussed on the slit of the spectrograph, the motions in the line of sight can be measured accurately in miles per second.

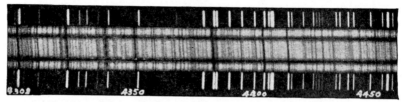

Fig. 113.—Spectrogram of Saturn and its rings.

The spectrum of the planet's disc shows in the center, the rings on either side and laboratory spectra at the top and bottom. Compare with diagram Figure 114. (*Spectrum by V. M. Slipher, Lowell Observatory. Courtesy Astronomical Society of the Pacific.*)

The tilt of the lines in the spectrum of Figure 113 displays the shifts in the wavelengths for various parts of the rings and the disc, and therefore the velocities in the line of sight. Note the reverse tilt of the lines in the rings as compared with the disc. At every point along the rings the measured velocity agrees exactly with that of a corresponding satellite if it were moving in a circular orbit. Kepler's laws of motion are obeyed precisely; the inner sections of the rings rotate more rapidly than the outer sections. Were the rings solid, the outer edges would move more rapidly than the inner. This demonstration of the discontinuous structure of Saturn's rings was performed in 1895 by J. E. Keeler at the Allegheny Observatory. A spectrogram made by V. M. Slipher at the Lowell Observatory and Keeler's diagram of the shifts of the spectral lines are shown in Figures 113 and 114 respectively.

The mass of the rings and the sizes of the particles can be only estimated. James Clerk Maxwell, the famous English physicist of last century, deduced an upper limit to the average space density of the rings. His theory is too involved for presentation here, but from it he concluded that the average density in the rings cannot exceed $\frac{1}{300}$ of the density of Saturn. In addition we know that the rings

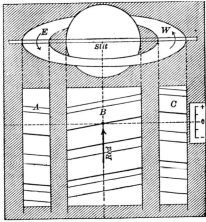

Fig. 114.—Rotation of Saturn and rings.

Diagram of spectrum to match Figure 113. Note tilts of the lines. The outer edges of the rings move more slowly than the inner. (*By J. E. Keeler, from C. A. Young's, "General Astronomy." Courtesy Ginn and Co.*)

reflect light excellently, better than natural rock surfaces. Material generally reflects better when pulverized than when in large pieces; therefore the particles of Saturn's rings are probably small, like ordinary dust, but not so small that light pressure might force them away. We can visualize the rings as consisting of broken rocks, pebbles and dust,* summing to a total of perhaps one millionth Saturn's mass, or less than a hundredth that of the Moon.

---

* Not as fine as white flour.

Saturn is a unique member of the solar system not only because of its rings but also because its average density is less than that of water (0.72)! For Saturn, the problems of a deep atmosphere are even more complicated than they were for Jupiter. In spite of the low average density, the distribution of matter in Saturn is much like that in Jupiter—highly concentrated towards the center. The period of rotation, only ten and a quarter hours,* and the polar flattening of ten per cent provide a measure of the concentration. The stony metallic core must, therefore, be quite small. It may contain only ten per cent of Saturn's mass—to be compared to forty or fifty per cent for Jupiter. Figure 115 illustrates a possible distribution of hydrogen, ice and rock.

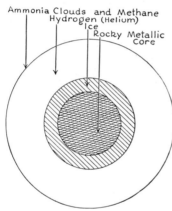

Ammonia Clouds and Methane
Hydrogen (Helium)
Ice
Rocky Metallic Core

Fig. 115.—The interior of Saturn.

According to R. Wildt.

The spectrograph reveals that Saturn's atmosphere contains more methane and less ammonia than Jupiter's. Since Saturn ($-243°F.$) is some $27°F.$ colder than Jupiter, we may well conclude that more of the ammonia has frozen out of its atmosphere and that the reflected sunlight penetrates a thicker layer of methane. The lower temperature may also explain the more sluggish changes in the cloud formations and less complex structural detail.

Large scale disturbances, however, are occasionally manifest in Saturn's atmosphere. The great white spot of 1933 is conspicuous in the first photograph of Figure 116; a year

---

* Determined by the spectrograph, and from the motions of rare spots.

later, in the second photograph, the spot is missing and has been replaced by a white equatorial band. During the interval the northern (lower) hemisphere has completely changed its superficial appearance. The similarities in the

Fig. 116.—Great white spot on Saturn.

(Left) In August 1933. (Right) White equatorial band in September 1934. (*Photographs by E. C. Slipher, Lowell Observatory.*)

atmospheric phenomena of Saturn and Jupiter are more striking than the differences, the latter being more in degree than in kind. This is true also of the colorings of the two planets, with the exception of an occasional greenish tint in Saturn's polar areas.

Fig. 117.—Saturn in different colors.

(Left) Red. (Middle) Blue. (Right) Yellow-green. Taken in 1940 with various filters and color-sensitive emulsions. (*Photograph by E. C. Slipher, Lowell Observatory.*)

The photographs of Figure 117 have registered Saturn's appearance in various colors of the spectrum. The white rings provide a ready standard for judging color shadings on the disc. Since the rings match the brilliancy of the equatorial belt in all three photographs, the belt must be white. The next band in the southern (upper) hemisphere is particularly dark in the blue but shows brilliantly in the red and fairly strongly in the yellow green. It is therefore orange yellow, somewhat more reddish than the area above it. A greenish cast in the polar region is suggested by the comparative polar flattening in the three colors. From year to year the shadings of color over Saturn's disc are observed to vary greatly.

From these observations of the motions and changes in the cloud formations on Saturn, we must conclude that great forces act within and beneath the cloud layers. Perhaps the forces in Saturn are less violent than those in Jupiter, but for both planets a solid and stable interior seems improbable.

Of Saturn's nine satellites, the most interesting is perhaps Japetus.* It, like several of the other satellites, rotates with the same face towards Saturn, but during a rotation of Japetus, its brightness varies by a factor of *five times*. Hence one side reflects light five times as well as the other; the surface structures of the two sides must be remarkably dissimilar. We might speculate that Japetus suffered disfiguration by a collision with some wandering member of the solar system, or perhaps was partially discolored by gaseous outbursts from Saturn during the early stages of evolution.

The most remote satellite, Phoebe, revolves in a retrograde orbit of eight million miles radius. When discovered by W. H. Pickering in 1898, it represented the only case of retrograde motion in a multiple system of satellites, but its claim to fame was later invalidated by the discoveries of Jupiter's three retrograde satellites. In the Saturn system the satellites are fairly similar in size and brightness; the faintest

---

* About half the Moon in diameter.

Blue   Green Yellow   Red   Infrared

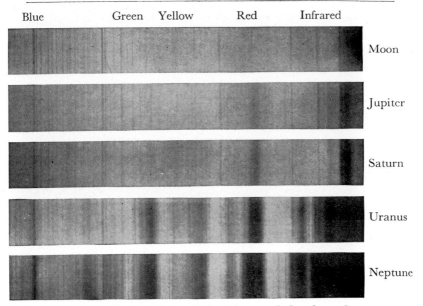

Moon

Jupiter

Saturn

Uranus

Neptune

Fig. 118.—Spectrograms of the Moon and the giant planets.
Note the great dark absorptions by methane gas, especially in Neptune's spectrum. (*Spectra by V. M. Slipher, Lowell Observatory.*)

and most recently discovered is again Phoebe, which is some fiftyfold brighter than the faintest in Jupiter's family. Since Jupiter possesses so many satellites, it is rather surprising that more faint members have not been discovered in Saturn's system.

URANUS AND NEPTUNE

These two planets are practically identical twins, giants in the outer regions of the solar system. Their diameters are about four times that of the Earth; Uranus is the larger by several hundred miles, although the measures are somewhat uncertain because of the hazy edges of the discs. Neptune, however, is the more massive, comprising seventeen and one sixth Earth masses while Uranus corresponds to fourteen and two thirds.

Although no surface markings have been observed on Neptune, perhaps because of the great distance, and only faint belts have been seen on Uranus, the planets are certainly enveloped with atmospheres resembling those of Jupiter and Saturn. The albedos, or reflecting powers, are high and the spectra show methane absorptions similar to those for Jupiter and Saturn, but much intensified. Observe the sequence of spectra in Figure 118. The absorptions of yellow and red light by methane vapor are so enormous for Uranus and Neptune that the planets appear greenish in color when observed directly; the color is more pronounced for Neptune. The spectrograms evidence only a trace of ammonia vapor, however.

A lack of gaseous ammonia and an abundance of methane are readily explained as resulting from the vast distances of these planets and the corresponding diminution in the amount of solar heat received at their surfaces. The sunlight is indeed so weak at Uranus that its surface temperature is less than $-300°F.$, while Neptune is probably some $30°F.$ colder. The temperature conditions on these outer planets are so extreme* that laboratory techniques can duplicate them only on a very small scale.

The increasing strength of the methane absorptions and the weakening of the ammonia absorptions as we progress from Jupiter to Neptune (note again Figure 118) certainly arise from the decrease in temperature. The vapor pressure of ammonia decreases very rapidly with temperature; hence precious little ammonia gas can remain in Neptune's atmosphere. Furthermore, with a decreased temperature, more of the ammonia crystals must settle out of the gaseous

---

* Not so far above the absolute zero at $-460°F.$

hydrogen strata, thereby reducing the number of clouds and bands, so conspicuous on Jupiter. Similarly, the interiors of the more distant and somewhat smaller planets are probably cooler. Thus the effects of internal eruptions or disturbances, such as Jupiter's Red Spot, are progressively less conspicuous on Saturn, Uranus and Neptune. Variations in surface color, too are less prevalent, none being observable on Neptune. The increased methane absorption with lowered temperature may result from greater penetration of sunlight into atmospheres less filled with clouds. The reflected light passes through thicker layers of methane.

The rotation periods of the twin giants must be determined by indirect methods because of the difficulty in observing surface markings on Uranus and the absence of markings on Neptune. Percival Lowell and V. M. Slipher, in 1912, first utilized the spectrograph to measure the speed of rotation for Uranus. They found that the spectral lines at the edges of the planet's disc were displaced by an amount corresponding to a speed of about ten and a half miles per second. From the known circumference they deduced that Uranus rotates in ten and three quarters hours. Three years later, Leon Campbell of the Harvard Observatory observed regular fluctuations in the brightness of Uranus and confirmed the spectrographic period.

Neptune's great distance reduces the size and brightness of its apparent disc to such an extent that the spectrograms are very difficult to obtain. At the Lick Observatory, J. H. Moore and D. H. Menzel obtained the value of 15.8 hours for the period of rotation, just twice the period of small variations observed in the light. Neptune apparently had two irregularities on opposite sides when the light fluctuations were measured.

Both Uranus and Neptune therefore rotate very rapidly. They are also flattened at the poles. Calculations from these data show that Uranus and Neptune are centrally condensed, like Jupiter and Saturn, and confirm the general opinion that the four planets are fundamentally similar. Jupiter, Uranus and Neptune are nearly identical in density, 1.34, 1.27 and 1.58 respectively, while Saturn, with its phenomenally low value, is somewhat anomalous as compared to the other three.

Uranus is anomalous in a different respect. The plane of rotation of the planet, which is also the plane of revolution for the four satellites, is tipped nearly at right angles to their plane of revolution about the Sun. In fact the plane is tipped slightly more than at right angles (98°), so that all the motions are technically retrograde. The four satellites are very faint, observable only in large telescopes, but are average in other respects. Their diameters range from perhaps four hundred to a thousand miles.

Neptune's one satellite is larger than the Moon* but is almost as faint as the brightest of Uranus' system, because of the increased distance. Its diameter, too small to be measured directly, is probably slightly over three thousand miles, of the same order as the Galilean satellites Ganymede and Callisto of Jupiter's system. The satellite moves in a retrograde direction about an orbit inclined some forty degrees to the plane of the planet's motion. Neptune's rotation however is direct, contrary to that of the satellite. We have here another anomaly to add to the growing collection of problems that must be solved by a satisfactory theory of planetary evolution.

We see that the giant planets are really very much alike, the major superficial differences being produced by the

---

* S. B. Nicholson, A. van Maanen, and H. C. Willis, of the Mount Wilson Observatory place its mass at $\frac{1}{16}$ the Earth's, with considerable uncertainty.

varying temperatures that arise from their positions in space. They all rotate rapidly, have huge atmospheres of methane and ammonia, and are composed of light materials highly concentrated towards the centers. In all these characteristics they differ from the terrestrial planets, Mercury, Venus, Earth, Mars and Pluto. The differences are so striking in every detail that it seems incongruous to associate these two groups of planets with the same system.

The giant planets, in spite of, or because of, their huge dimensions, provide no possible abode conducive to life of any kind now known. We must study the terrestrial planets if we hope to attribute universality to the ethereal phenomenon of life.

12

THE TERRESTRIAL PLANETS— PLUTO, MERCURY AND VENUS

PLUTO

THE MOST DISTANT PLANET AS YET DISCOVERED BELONGS to a species entirely different from that of the other planets in these outer regions. Pluto appears to be a dwarf interloper among the giants. Our knowledge of Pluto is meager but sufficient to establish some very pertinent facts. Besides the orbit and consequent distance we know Pluto's brightness, color and approximate mass.* From these facts alone we must deduce all that we can about its character. The conclusions are surprisingly definite.

Since the mass of Pluto is nearly as great as that of the Earth, let us assume that Pluto equals the Earth in size and that it reflects sunlight exactly as the Moon does (i.e., poorly). A simple calculation, based on the inverse square law of light decrease with distance, shows that our hypothetical Pluto would be more than twice as bright as the

---

* The discovery of Pluto and the determination of its mass were discussed in Chapters 3 and 4.

real one. If Pluto is actually denser than the Earth, but with nearly the same mass, it must be smaller and reflect less light than we have assumed. The discrepancy is therefore reduced. On the other hand, the discrepancy can also be removed if Pluto's surface reflects light less efficiently than the Moon.

These two possibilities, that Pluto is denser than the Earth or reflects light less efficiently than the Moon, seem reasonable enough, until we note that the Earth is the densest body in the solar system, five and a half times as dense as water, while the Moon, with an albedo of about seven per cent, is the poorest reflector. We are forced to conclude either that Pluto is composed of materials heavier than solid iron (7.8 times the density of water) or else that it reflects no more than four or five per cent of the sunlight that falls upon it. Only very dark or almost black objects reflect as poorly as this. Pluto's surface must therefore reflect similarly to our darkest rocks or the planet must consist of heavy substances.

If iron were sufficiently dense to satisfy the requirements there would be little objection to the hypothesis that Pluto consists largely of iron. This metal constitutes an appreciable fraction of the Earth's mass and is abundant in the surface gases of the Sun and many other stars. Metals and substances denser than iron, however, appear to be rare in the stars as well as on the Earth.* The evidence suggests that Pluto would truly be abnormal were it composed of materials denser than iron. A more reasonable alternative would be to suspect the accuracy of some of the fundamental data.

Whatever its internal structure, Pluto cannot be a good reflector and therefore, like the other poor reflectors, can

---

* Although the great weight of lead, gold and the heavier substances may cause them to sink below the observable surfaces of the stars.

possess little or no atmosphere. Its temperature is probably less than $-348°F.$, only about a hundred degrees from the absolute zero. Most of the common gases would liquefy or freeze out of an atmosphere at this low temperature. Were Pluto a better reflector we might imagine it covered with an ocean of liquid oxygen or nitrogen.* The surface of the planet, however, is probably very rough, like the Moon's, but, of course, we cannot ascertain the presence of craters. From the yellowish-white color we know that the surface is not covered with highly pigmented materials, and from its poor reflectivity, that fine dust or white crystalline substances are absent.

Pluto is undoubtedly an arid, frigid and dark world, similar to the Earth in size and mass, but inhospitable beyond comprehension.

MERCURY

Mercury is the fourth brightest planet, at its best nearly equalling Sirius in brilliancy and being exceeded only by Venus, Mars and Jupiter. Nevertheless, Mercury is a very difficult object to observe because of its small orbit and concomitant proximity to the Sun; the greatest possible *elongation*† is twenty-eight degrees. At this most favorable position the phase corresponds to the quarter moon; the full phase occurs at *superior conjunction* when Mercury lies beyond the Sun, nearly in line with it. After sunset or before sunrise Mercury is always very low in the sky, a situation that limits night observations to a short interval. In addition, the turbulence of our atmosphere at low altitudes produces

---

* Oxygen, of course, is too active chemically ever to form an ocean by itself. Hydrogen and helium would be gaseous on Pluto, and, therefore, must be absent.

† Elongation is the angular distance from the Sun as seen from the Earth. Planetary configurations are shown in Figure 140, Appendix II.

poor "seeing." Hence Mercury, to a great extent, is observed in full daylight, scattered sunlight being eliminated as much as possible by suitable screens.

Because of these various difficulties only the most expert observers have been able to detect surface markings on Mercury. Schiaparelli and Barnard,* two great observers of the last century, each sketched vague surface detail, not in excellent agreement. Schiaparelli's map is reproduced in Figure 119. Since the lunar photographs have shown that certain markings on the Moon, particularly the rays and to some extent the maria, are more conspicuous when the Moon is full, it is of considerable interest that Barnard described the markings on Mercury as generally similar to the maria on the Moon, and that Schiaparelli obtained his best results when the planet was at its full phase, close to the Sun.

In recent years extensive observations of Mercury have been made by E. M. Antoniadi at Meudon, France. His map is shown in Figure 120. A comparison with Figure 119, at first glance, suggests that Schiaparelli and Antoniadi disagree in their observations, but a closer inspection brings out the essential agreement. No two individuals draw a poorly defined object in the same manner. To demonstrate this important fact of observational astronomy, place one of these maps at a distance where details are barely distinguishable and draw what you see. Comparison of the drawing with the original may be surprising.

Schiaparelli's opinion that the markings are stationary on the apparent disc is shared by Antoniadi and is accepted by the majority of astronomers. Hence Mercury rotates slowly on its axis with the same face always towards the Sun except for minor librations. The period of rotation is

---

* Italian and American astronomers, respectively.

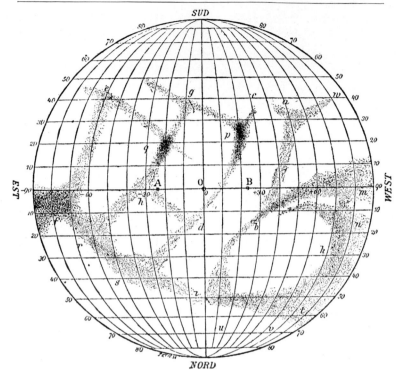

Fig. 119.—Schiaparelli's map of Mercury.
(*From Antoniadi's "La Planète Mercure." Courtesy Gauthier-Villars, Paris.*)

88 days, equal to the sidereal period of revolution about the Sun. Because only one face of the planet is lighted, the drawings of Figures 119 and 120 show only one hemisphere.

The existence of even a trace of atmosphere on Mercury is somewhat doubtful. Schiaparelli and Antoniadi agree that faint whitish clouds often obscure the darker markings. Such observations, however, are of a negative character—a failure to see very indistinct markings—and permit one to reserve an opinion concerning the reality of the clouds.

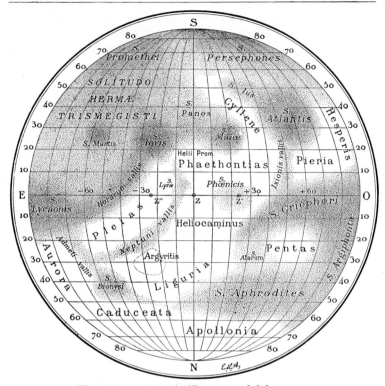

Fig. 120.—Antoniadi's map of Mercury.
(*From Antoniadi's "La Planète Mercure." Courtesy Gauthier-Villars, Paris.*)

Mercury's low albedo, comparable to the Moon's, is conclusive evidence that any possible atmosphere is thin. Furthermore, the velocity of escape is only 2.3 miles per second,* insufficient for the retention of gases, especially as the molecules would be activated by the intense heat from the nearby Sun. Perhaps even better evidence disproving the existence of an atmosphere is given by the observations

---

* Molecules travelling faster than this could escape forever from Mercury's gravitational attraction. See Chapter 9, page 139.

made when Mercury is in the crescent phase. The horns of the crescent do not appear to extend beyond their geometric limits. Any twilight effect of scattering or refraction in an atmosphere would produce an apparent extension of the horns towards the unlighted portion of the disc.

If, then, there is no appreciable atmosphere on Mercury, and the planet keeps the same face always towards the Sun, we may conclude that Mercury is simultaneously both the hottest and the coldest planetary member of the Sun's family. At the center of the perpetually sunlit face the temperature rises (at perihelion) to about 770°F., according to determinations by Edison Pettit and Seth B. Nicholson of the Mount Wilson Observatory. By means of delicate instruments,* these investigators measured the heat (or infrared light) emitted by the hot surface, and were therefore able to calculate the temperature. At 770°F. both tin and lead are molten and even zinc is near its melting point (786°F.). Mercury rather than Pluto might well have been named after the god of the underworld!

The exceedingly high temperatures on Mercury's sunlit side are contrasted with immeasurably low temperatures on the perpetually dark side. No heat can reach the dark side except by conduction through the rocky core, an extremely slow process, or conceivably by convection currents in a residual trace of atmosphere. The temperature of the unlighted hemisphere must be near the absolute zero, colder even than Pluto. Thus Mercury exhibits a dual personality, representing both extremes of planetary temperatures.

The great similarity of Mercury to the Moon has been indicated by its size, mode of rotation, lack of atmosphere

---

* A vacuum thermocouple and subsidiary instruments with the 100-inch reflector. Since the maximum energy of sunlight is in the visual spectrum, the energy in the far infrared measures the radiation from the planet itself, i.e., the temperature.

and superficial appearance. Its mean density is only slightly greater than the Moon's, 3.8 as compared to 3.3, so that the internal structure is probably similar also. The two bodies reflect light in practically an identical fashion with respect both to color and to intensity at various angles of reflection. Light rays falling perpendicularly to the surface are reflected back along their paths with fair efficiency but are reflected at great angles very poorly. Even the *polarization*, or plane of vibration, of the reflected light is the same for Mercury as for the Moon. Hence we may conclude that the surface of Mercury resembles the Moon's in detail as well as in general character. Certainly the exterior of Mercury is irregular and rough.

Mercury, therefore, can best be visualized as an oversized edition of the Moon. Its chief points of interest arise from its proximity to the Sun and the resultant extremes of temperature, short period of revolution and rapidity of motion, some 36 miles per second at maximum.*

VENUS

Venus is both the "evening star" and the "morning star," Hesperus and Phosphorus of antiquity. It is the most brilliant object in the sky, except for the Sun and Moon. Venus is often visible in the daylight and capable of casting shadows at night. Only 144 days elapse from the evening elongation, when Venus is the first object to be found in the evening twilight, until the morning elongation when it is the last "star" to disappear in the Sun's morning glow, while 440 days are required for Venus to revolve beyond the Sun and return again to its evening elongation.†

---

* Mercury's greatest contribution to science has arisen from this rapidity of motion, which has made possible one of the three astronomical proofs of the Einstein theory of general relativity.

† The geometry can be seen in Figure 4, Chapter 1.

The magnification of even a small telescope suffices to resolve the brilliant point of light into a silvery disc, somewhat diffuse at the edges because of the unsteadiness of our atmosphere, but showing the crescent phases like the Moon. When the crescent is thin the horns appear to extend more than half around the disc, as though the irradiation of the brilliant surface were producing an optical illusion. In the extreme situation, however, when Venus lies nearly in

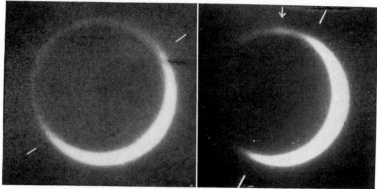

Fig. 121.—Twilight arc around Venus.

Note the extension of the crescent completely around the disc in the first photograph and the bright extension at the arrow in the second. 1938. (*Photographs by E. C. Slipher, Lowell Observatory.*)

the line between us and the Sun, a faint circle of light can be seen entirely around the disc. This twilight arc is shown in the photographs of Figure 121. Neither our atmosphere nor an optical defect could produce this phenomenon. A deep atmosphere on Venus must deflect the sunlight around the edges of the disc by refraction.

But why do we not see clouds in the atmosphere or else surface markings on the globe itself? Under the best observing conditions, when our atmosphere is clear and steady, only the haziest suggestions of markings can be seen by the most expert observers—"large dusky spots" as Barnard called them. These faint patches, too indefinite to be drawn, appear impermanent. Photographs in the long wavelengths of infrared light have also proved unsuccessful in registering

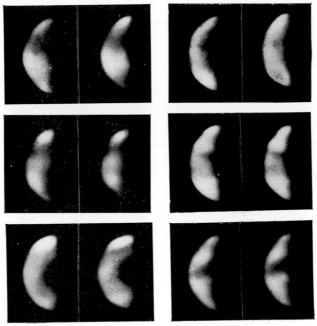

Fig. 122.—Venus in ultraviolet light.

Each pair of images was made on the same night, the two top pairs on successive nights, and the two middle pairs on successive nights. Note the changes from night to night. (*Photographs by F. E. Ross, Mount Wilson Observatory.*)

details, notwithstanding the "haze penetrating" power of the infrared filters and light. It was not until Frank E. Ross* experimented with the other extreme of the color spectrum, ultraviolet light, that details on Venus could be photo-

---

* Using the 60-inch and 100-inch reflectors at the Mount Wilson Observatory.

graphed. To everyone's surprise, because ultraviolet light is markedly useless for clouds on the Earth, Ross was successful in registering great hazy cloudlike formations in the atmosphere of Venus.

Ross's photographs in Figure 122 show that these dark hazy patches change their structures from day to day, proving that they do not represent permanent features of the planet's surface, but that they are probably clouds, floating in the sky of Venus. Their changing forms make it impossible to measure the rotation of the planet by day-to-day observations; no evidence for rotation can be obtained in the short intervals of continuous observation. Thus the rate of rotation must be found in some other fashion. Again the spectrograph was called into use, but no shifts in the absorption lines could be detected even with the superb observing techniques utilized at the Mount Wilson Observatory. The speed of rotation, therefore, must be very slow, not less than two or three of our weeks for one day on Venus.

Since Venus rotates so slowly, we might be tempted to conclude that Venus, like Mercury, keeps one face always towards the Sun. If this hypothesis were correct we should expect that the dark side would be exceedingly cold. Pettit and Nicholson have measured the temperature of the dark side of Venus. They find that the temperature is not low, its value being only $-9°F.$, much warmer than our stratosphere in broad daylight. It is unlikely that atmospheric currents from the bright side of Venus could perpetually heat the dark side. The planet must rotate fairly often to keep the dark side from cooling excessively. We may conclude, therefore, that Venus turns on its axis within a period less than 225 days (one revolution about the Sun) but greater than two or three weeks. The actual period is probably near the lower limit. One day on Venus may correspond to a month, more or less, of terrestrial time.

Although the dark side of Venus is not cold, the sunlit side is not particularly warm. It radiates at a temperature of from 120°F. to 140°F., comparable to a warm day on a terrestrial desert rather than a warm day on Mercury when lead and tin melt. Obviously the atmosphere must be thick to regulate the temperatures so effectively, particularly as the measurements of temperature apply to the high regions of the atmosphere above the cloud banks. Calculations based upon the extension of the horns at the crescent phase show that the refractive atmosphere extends for one to five miles above the visible surface. The atmosphere undoubtedly exists at much greater heights, but there it is exceedingly rare.

Further confirmation of the supposition that the visible surface of Venus is the top of a cloudbank is evidenced by the color of the reflected light, the high albedo or reflectivity, and the manner in which the brilliancy varies over the apparent disc. The silvery white color of the planet and these other observational data can be explained only if the light is reflected from globules of liquid or solid material. Reflection from a very thick layer of gas alone, or from a layer of gas filled with dust, would redden the planet by absorbing the blue light. Since the reflecting surface must be composed of globules, and since the surface features change fairly rapidly, there is no alternative to the hypothesis of an actual layer of clouds.

Because the cloud layer is impenetrable by light rays, our studies must be confined to the clouds themselves and to the gas layer above them. The spectrograph provides definite but perhaps disappointing information about the composition of the gas. No evidence for oxygen or water vapor has been found. St. John and Nicholson of the Mount Wilson Observatory have demonstrated that the sunlight reflected from Venus passes through less than the equivalent of a yard of oxygen gas at sea level pressure on the Earth, or less than a thousandth part of the oxygen in our atmosphere. In addition, the amount of water vapor above the clouds on Venus is less than that in our atmosphere by at least a factor of ten. These values represent upper limits to the quantities of oxygen and water vapor actually present in the atmosphere of Venus; there may be less of either gas or none whatsoever.

Adams and Dunham,* however, obtained more positive results from their spectrographic analysis. They discovered new infrared absorptions that were unknown from laboratory studies. Calculations indicated that the unknown absorptions might arise from ordinary carbon dioxide, if the light passes through a sufficiently long column of this gas. To check the theory Dunham filled a sixty-foot pipe with carbon dioxide compressed to ten times the pressure of our atmosphere. When artificial light was sent down the tube and reflected back to the same spectrograph used for the Venus spectra, identical absorptions were obtained. One of his spectrograms is compared with the solar spectrum in Figure 123.

There can be no doubt that an enormous amount of carbon dioxide is present above the cloud banks on Venus. The quantity there corresponds to a column of the pure gas at sea level pressure, some twelve hundred feet to two miles† in length, many times the amount present in our atmosphere. How much more carbon dioxide may lie beneath the clouds is a matter of speculation.

Hitherto in our travels through the solar system we have encountered planetary exteriors that are completely undesirable for home sites. The distant planets are too cold; Mercury is both too hot and too cold. The giant planets are

---

* At the Mount Wilson Observatory.
† The second estimate made by Adel and Slipher at the Lowell Observatory.

covered with noxious or poisonous gases and may even lack solid surfaces; Pluto and Mercury and the many satellites have no atmospheres whatsoever. When, at last, we do find a comfortably heated planet with an atmosphere, we discover that there is no water and no oxygen—nothing but smothering carbon dioxide! Mars is the only remaining hope for the possibility of our kind of life on another planet.

But is there not some chance that conditions may be more favorable beneath the opaque clouds on Venus? This question is worthy of discussion, although we can rarely be

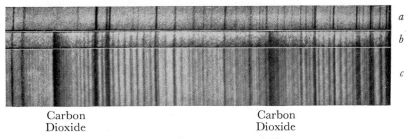

a

b

c

Carbon Dioxide   Carbon Dioxide

Fig. 123.—Spectrograms of Venus.

(*a*) Sun. (*b*) Venus. (*c*) Venus widened. Note the infrared absorptions of carbon dioxide, strong in the spectra of Venus, but absent in the spectrum of the Sun. (*Spectra by T. Dunham. Courtesy Astronomical Society of the Pacific.*)

absolutely certain of deductions concerning unobservable physical conditions. Our first problem concerns the nature of the clouds themselves. Until recently, for want of a better theory, the clouds were commonly assumed to be ordinary clouds of water droplets, similar to those on the Earth. No one was satisfied with this theory because of the absence of appreciable water vapor. At the prevalent noon temperatures on Venus, evaporation should release a considerable amount of water vapor into the upper atmosphere. Although some physical explanation may be found for this lack of water vapor, Rupert Wildt has put forward an alternative explanation for the deficiency. He shows that the clouds may not consist of water after all, but of formaldehyde!

Wildt's surprising suggestion is based on the chemical fact that in a mixture of carbon dioxide and water vapor, formaldehyde is formed by the action of ultraviolet light.* The process liberates free oxygen gas. In Wildt's theory the excess oxygen must be removed from Venus' atmosphere or two important difficulties will result. In the first place no oxygen is observed in the spectrum of Venus; hence the theory collapses if the oxygen is not removed. Secondly, oxygen will eventually stop the process by absorbing the ultraviolet light necessary for the formaldehyde reaction. In our own atmosphere the reaction cannot occur because of the great blanket of oxygen,† absolutely opaque in the far ultraviolet.

To see what may happen to the free oxygen released in the formation of formaldehyde, we note that the surface of Venus may be very hot, even above the boiling point of water. This conclusion follows from a property of carbon dioxide. The gas is very transparent to all visual light, and unlike oxygen, to ultraviolet light. Carbon dioxide, however, absorbs heat (or far infrared) radiation very well. The result is that a greenhouse effect should be remarkably powerful in heating the surface of Venus. Much of the Sun's energy can enter as visual light, but the radiation from the heated surface is trapped by the carbon dioxide. This identical process helps to regulate the surface temperature of the Earth.

If the actual surface of Venus is heated, perhaps sufficiently to boil water, the free oxygen can easily combine

---

* The reaction is $CO_2 + H_2O = CH_2O + O_2$. Ultraviolet light furnishes the energy for the reaction.

† As the ordinary gas, O_2, and as ozone, O_3.

with the surface rock, particularly with iron compounds, to produce weathering, a process that has acted slowly on the Earth to use up enormous quantities of oxygen. Free oxygen is not a difficult substance to remove from any atmosphere, especially a heated one. Oxygen is very active chemically, combining with almost any element when there is the slightest opportunity; and heat activates the process. If vegetation did not replenish the supply, little if any oxygen might now remain in the Earth's atmosphere. Hence the problem of accounting for the slow removal of free oxygen from the atmosphere of Venus is not difficult.

The manufacture of formaldehyde on Venus by the combination of carbon dioxide and water can proceed so long as the water supply continues. A certain amount of water is also required for the formation of clouds. Pure formaldehyde gas is colorless and unclouded. The slightest trace of water vapor added to a flask of formaldehyde, however, instantly produces a thick white cloud. Huge chains of molecules form to produce droplets of the ordinary plastics that are now so important in industry. It is disconcerting to find that Venus may have been covered with plastics for millions of years while on Earth we have just discovered them.

One questionable point of Wildt's theory of the formaldehyde plastic clouds still remains. Why do we not observe the characteristic absorption bands of formaldehyde in the spectrum of Venus? After a careful search Wildt found no evidence for them. His explanation is simple. The formaldehyde in the droplet or plastic state does not vaporize easily at the moderate temperatures on Venus. Probably at very low levels in the atmosphere, where the temperature is higher, enough vaporization occurs to maintain the clouds. In the high levels we should not expect to find formaldehyde vapor, although we should expect water vapor were the clouds composed of water droplets.

To explain the difference between the conditions on Venus and on the Earth we must postulate that the surface of Venus originally possessed relatively less water than the Earth's surface, that no great seas are present, or ever were present. Even more fundamentally, hydrogen was perhaps less abundant on Venus; the oxygen combined with the more abundant carbon to form carbon dioxide rather than with the less abundant hydrogen to form water, as on the Earth. On this assumption, the hydrogen on Venus is locked up in the plastics rather than in water.

The preceding picture of conditions on Venus is still speculative, subject to critical analysis and to critical observations. The theory is, nevertheless, most ingenious and thought provoking. Correct or not it is another milestone on the road to a further understanding of the Earth's "sister" planet, Venus. We may well be amazed to learn that two planets, so nearly identical in size and mass, can possess such radically different surfaces, the one covered with oceans of water, the other with clouds or perhaps oceans of plastics!

13

MARS

MARS WAS NAMED FOR THE GOD OF WAR BECAUSE OF THE planet's sanguine color, obvious to the naked eye and more conspicuous with a telescope. The name, unfortunately, was much too appropriate during a number of years near the turn of this century. An astronomical battle was raging at that time and Mars was the battlefield. On one side was Percival Lowell, who carried on the banner first raised by Schiaparelli. On the other side stood a considerable fraction of the astronomical world. The *casus belli* was the observation of canals* on Mars by both Schiaparelli and Lowell and their interpretation of these narrow markings as artificial waterways. Some of Lowell's composite drawings are shown in Figure 124.

In the scientific world disagreement among the authorities contributes to real and substantial progress. Usually the contenders are each partially right and each partially wrong, but the heat of discussion furthers observation, which

---

* Schiaparelli used the Italian word *canali*, which means primarily *channels* or *grooves* and secondarily manmade waterways. Lowell based his interpretation on his own extensive observations of Mars.

is the foundation of science. The Martian battle is over and the smoke has cleared.* We can hardly say that either side won a decided victory, but these assiduous observers, seeking the truth, have increased our knowledge of Mars and helped to place its study on a firm basis.

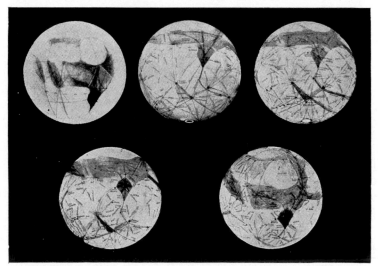

Fig. 124.—Lowell's maps of Mars.

For the years 1894, 1901, 1903, 1905, 1907 from left to right, respectively. Drawn on globes and photographed. (*Courtesy of the Lowell Observatory.*)

When Mars is most favorably situated for observation, a magnification of some seventy times enlarges the disc to the apparent diameter of the Moon. Small telescopes can be used satisfactorily at such a magnifying power while larger ones are efficient at much greater powers. Since considerable detail on the Moon is visible to the naked eye, the

---

* The story of this battle of words has not received a thorough historical treatment. The present writer makes no pretense of completeness in allotting credit for the various concepts involved.

reader may wonder why Mars should be difficult to observe. The difficulty is again the "seeing," discussed in Chapter 8. The remarkable observations made of Mars and the other planets by astronomers at the Lowell, Lick and Mount Wilson Observatories were possible because of the excellent "seeing" conditions at these places.

Even as first observed with a small telescope under very ordinary conditions of "seeing," Mars immediately gains an individuality. Lowell wrote: "Almost as soon as magnification gives Mars a disk, that disk shows markings, white spots crowning a globe spread with blue-green patches on an orange ground." * This verbal picture of Mars is somewhat more striking than the sensory registration of a novice who first observes Mars with a small telescope under average conditions. But by persistent observation, night after night, his eye will become more and more expert until it is able to distinguish surface details that were at first completely invisible. This remarkable improvement of visual acuity with experience has sometimes been underestimated, even by skilled observers who have not concentrated on planetary observations.

Three prerequisites are thus essential to a satisfactory study of the surface features on Mars: ideal atmospheric conditions, a "perfect eye," and a first-quality telescope, not necessarily a large one. † With these prerequisites the expert observer of Mars must then continue his observations every clear night at every opposition of the planet for several years. Only under these circumstances can he hope to see "all there is to see" on the Martian surface. Naturally there have been few observers who have possessed both the per

---

* From "Mars and its Canals," page 32. The Macmillan Co.

† Beyond an aperture of twelve to fifteen inches there is little gain. The great 200-inch reflector, invaluable in certain studies, cannot much improve the direct visual observations of Mars.

severance and the opportunity for exhaustive studies of Mars. Schiaparelli and Lowell have provided most of the basic visual observations.

In recent years, however, the art of planetary photography has progressed to the stage where the major surface markings of Mars can be registered by photographic emulsions for future study. Furthermore, color screens and various color-sensitive emulsions permit photography in the various colors to which the eye is sensitive and also in the ultraviolet and infrared regions of the spectrum, invisible to the eye. Such observers as E. C. Slipher of the Lowell Observatory and W. H. Wright and R. J. Trumpler at the Lick Observatory have been able to make new deductions about the character of the Martian atmosphere from their photographs, and to show the pictorial evidence to the world for impartial criticism. The visual observations are essential for a record of only the finest details. No longer must the astronomer and layman depend wholly upon both the skill and judgment of a few observers of Mars. We still depend upon the skill of a few, but may, to a large measure, judge for ourselves the certainty of their conclusions.

Mars can be well observed at intervals of about two years and fifty days* when it comes into opposition with the Sun. Its distance from the Earth at opposition varies by a factor of nearly two† because of the high eccentricity of the Martian orbit. The most favorable oppositions for observation are, of course, those at which Mars is the nearest, i.e., when opposition occurs at perihelion. Since oppositions occur successively later by fifty days on alternate years, a favorable opposition will be repeated in seven or eight periods, at intervals of fifteen or seventeen years. The

---

* The synodic period with respect to the Earth is $780^d.0$; the sidereal period with respect to the stars is $687^d.0$. See Appendix III, also II.

† From 34,600,000 miles to 62,900,000 miles.

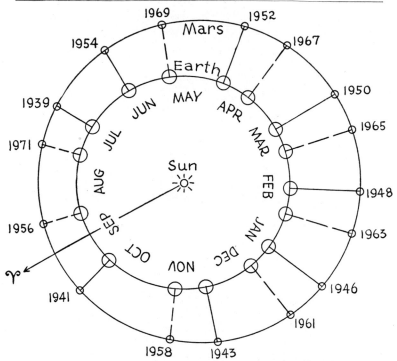

Fig. 125.—Oppositions of Mars from the Earth.

From 1939 to 1971. The relative distances are shown by the straight lines joining the orbits. The seasonal dates on the Earth are indicated. Mars is north of the equator for oppositions from September to March. The data were taken from the Planet Finder, Appendix V.

perihelion of Mars' orbit is so oriented that Mars is always best located for observation in August (1939, 1956, 1971). The positions of Mars at various oppositions are shown in Figure 125.

The equator of Mars, like the Earth's, is tipped some twenty-five degrees to the plane of its orbit, the direction of the poles remaining fixed in space. Consequently, at the times of Mars' closest approach we always see the planet in the same relative position. The south polar cap, by chance, is the one to be observed best, the north polar cap being turned towards us at the less favorable oppositions.

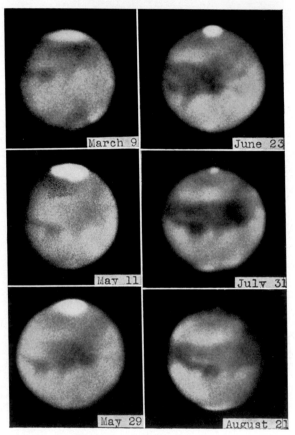

Fig. 126.—Seasons on Mars.

The dates given are Martian seasonal dates, taken to correspond to those on the Earth. (*Photographs by E. C. Slipher, Lowell Observatory.*)

The Martian day is just 37 m. 22.58 s. longer than our day. The rotation may be noticed after less than an hour's observing. On the succeeding night the planet presents the same side because it has completed a revolution in the meantime. Over an interval of about forty days the Earth gains a whole revolution, sufficient to complete a cycle of observations entirely around the planet. Similarly, in twenty-four hours, observers distributed around the Earth can observe the total circumference of Mars.

Photographically or visually the polar caps are usually the most conspicuous markings on the planet. The seasonal

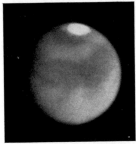 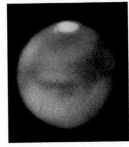

Fig. 127.—Mountains of Mitchell.

Photographs of Mars in 1909 and 1924. The detached area of the Martian polar cap appears at about the Martian date June 3. (*Photographs by E. C. Slipher, Lowell Observatory.*)

changes, first noted by Sir William Herschel, are regular, and even predictable with considerable accuracy. As the autumn season gives way to winter on one hemisphere of Mars, the corresponding polar cap grows irregularly until it may extend nearly halfway to the equator. With the coming of spring (in the Martian March), the cap begins to recede; by the end of the Martian July it has disappeared on that hemisphere. The opposite hemisphere is undergoing simultaneously the reverse cycle of changes. In Figure 126, E. C. Slipher's excellent photographs, which present the same side of the planet, show the recession of the south polar cap. The seasonal dates for Mars are taken to correspond to seasons on the Earth; it must be remembered that the Martian year is 687 days, equal to nearly two Earth years. From a careful inspection of the series of photographs we can see the general darkening around the white area as the cap wanes in March and May, the intensification of the dark areas progressively away from the pole in June and July, and their fading by August. This sequence of events is repeated almost identically every Martian year.

Even small details in the surface markings will reappear at the same season in different years. A detached area of the south polar cap is visible in the two photographs of Figure 127. The first photograph was taken in 1909 and the second in 1924, but both on the Martian date June 3. The persistent area bears the name, Mountains of Mitchell.*

The repetitive character of the changes in the polar caps suggests immediately that these white areas are snow, which melts as the temperature rises. An alternative material is carbon dioxide or dry ice. Temperature measures,† however, show that the temperature at the poles rises above the melting point of water in midsummer; this observation leaves us with the attractive probability that *the Martian polar caps are really snow*. The layer cannot be very thick because the Sun's heat, only forty per cent as great on Mars as on the Earth, would be insufficient to melt and evaporate a great quantity of snow. The maximum thickness may be only a few inches.

As a polar cap begins to form in the Martian autumn, variable clouds can be observed. The first two photographs

---

* There is some question whether the snow remains on a higher level or on a southerly slope. The Flagstaff observers favor the slope because of the low density gradient in the Martian atmosphere. The change in water-carrying power with altitude might be less than on the Earth. See later discussion for heights of Martian features.

† At the Lowell and Mount Wilson Observatories.

in Figure 128 were taken on successive nights in 1939 by E. C. Slipher, who went to South Africa to observe the planet at its close approach.* A white cloud near the south pole in (a), bottom, has disappeared by the next night (b). Another cloud is present six nights later (c). The question whether

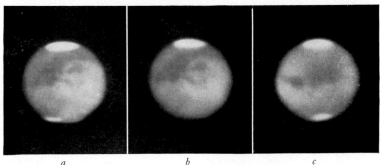

a　　　　　　　　　b　　　　　　　　　c

Fig. 128.—Clouds at the north pole of Mars.

(a). Shows cloud near the north pole, bottom. (b). Cloud has vanished on the next night. (c). Another cloud six days later. 1939. (*Photographs by E. C. Slipher, Lowell Observatory.*)

these variable markings are clouds in the atmosphere or frost on the ground can be answered fairly well by observations in light of different colors.

Infrared light can penetrate haze and dust in the Earth's atmosphere where blue or violet light will be stopped. Figure 129 presents the now famous photographs taken by W. H. Wright at the Lick Observatory. At the left are Mars and the Valley of San José as photographed by violet light, while on the right infrared light has been used. These photographs tell their own story. There can be little question that Mars is covered with a hazy atmosphere.

---

* Mars could be observed nearly overhead from the southern hemisphere. Dr. Slipher used the 27-inch refractor of the Yale Lamont-Hussey Observatory at Bloemfontein, South Africa, for these and other 1939 photographs shown in this book.

The variable white markings such as the ones in Figure 128, are bright in violet light and invisible in the infrared. They are probably thin clouds of water or ice crystals that reflect the violet light but transmit the infrared. Since the semipermanent polar caps are photographed in both colors

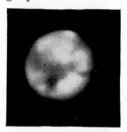

Fig. 129.—Mars and the valley of San José.

As photographed from Lick Observatory. Violet light was used in the left photographs and infrared light in the right. (*Photographs by W. H. Wright, Lick Observatory.*)

but are brighter in violet light, they must be actual surface deposits, accompanied by hazy or mistlike clouds. The top three photographs of Figure 130 illustrate the phenomenon. The colors, from left to right, are violet, infrared and yellow respectively. Note the brightness of the polar cap in the violet as compared with the infrared.

The bottom three photographs of Figure 130 demonstrate another effect that serves to confirm the previous conclusions. The apparent diameter of Mars is greater in violet than in infrared light. To what extent this observation results from "seeing" and photographic effects, it is difficult to say, but taken at its face value the observations require that the Martian atmosphere be 60 miles deep. *

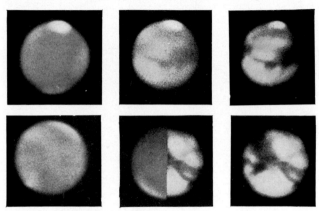

Fig. 130.—Mars in various colors.

Upper left, violet. Middle, infrared. Right, yellow. Lower left, ultraviolet. Right, infrared. Middle, half ultraviolet, half infrared. (*Photographs by W. H. Wright, Lick Observatory.*)

It has been suggested that the lack of detail in the blue or violet photographs of Mars, arise, not from atmospheric absorption but from a monotony of color on the Martian surface in the blue and violet light. Figure 131 portrays four photographs taken by E. C. Slipher in 1937. The upper left photograph was taken with red light and the others, at various times, with blue light. The two left photographs were made on the same night and show how surface features are occasionally visible in blue light. The atmospheric

* W. H. Wright's value.

haze clears at rare intervals to permit the blue light to penetrate. There can be no question that the blue and violet rays are ordinarily blocked by the atmosphere of Mars.

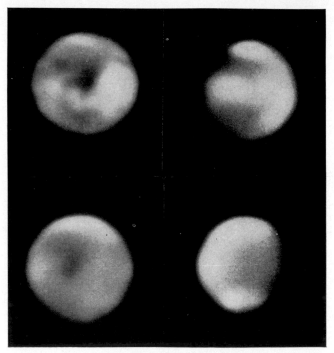

Fig. 131.—The haze cleared on Mars.

Same face of planet on different nights of 1937. Upper left, red light. Others, blue light. Note that on the lower left image surface markings are visible. (*Photographs by E. C. Slipher, Lowell Observatory.*)

Clouds like those seen near the polar caps are frequently observed on other parts of Mars' disc. These "blue" clouds are bright in blue and violet light but invisible in the infrared. They persist for only a few hours. The formation of such a cloud during a Martian afternoon is depicted by the series of photographs in Figure 132. The images are duplicated with identification arrows. As Mars rotates through about fifty-five degrees, the cloud, which is not present in the first photograph, is seen to develop and traverse the disc. It is brightest near sunset.

Besides the "blue" clouds, which are probably a thin mist, there are occasional yellow clouds, which are invisible in violet and ultraviolet light. The yellow clouds may persist for several days. W. H. Wright and R. J. Trumpler favor the

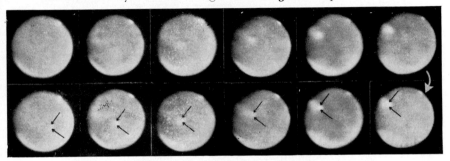

Fig. 132.—A Martian afternoon.

The arrows indicate a cloud that developed on the successive photographs. Mars turned towards the left during the four hours interval. The two rows of images are identical except for the arrows. (*Photographs by the Lick and Mount Wilson Observatories.*)

theory that the yellow clouds occur low in the Martian atmosphere where the violet light does not penetrate. The Flagstaff observers interpret the yellow clouds as dust. It is clear that the two interpretations are not mutually exclusive.

If the "blue" clouds are mist and the polar caps are snow, which is carried by the atmosphere from pole to pole during alternate seasons, we should expect water vapor to be observable in the Martian atmosphere. Most thorough studies have failed to indicate the slightest trace of water. Spectrograms have been made when the relative velocity between the Earth and Mars was at maximum, in order that any absorption lines of water vapor in Mars might be shifted away* from the corresponding lines produced by our own atmosphere, but to no avail. Adams and Dunham have concluded that the atmosphere of Mars contains less than five per cent the amount in our atmosphere. The test

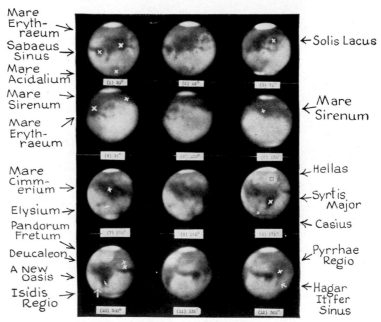

Fig. 133.—A panorama of Mars.

These photographs of Mars in 1939, show the planet turned successively through about thirty degrees. (*Photograph by E. C. Slipher, Lowell Observatory.*)

for oxygen is more sensitive than that for water vapor but still gives negative results. These same investigators place the oxygen content of Mars' atmosphere at less than a tenth of a per cent of the Earth's. There is enormously more oxygen above Mt. Everest than above the surface of Mars.

*The shift of spectral lines by radial velocity has been described in Chapter 11, page 177.

The dearth of water vapor, as indicated by the spectrograph, does not exclude the deduction that the polar caps are snow, but it does seriously limit estimates of the quantity present. Mars' atmosphere is certainly rare, in spite of the possible sixty-mile depth. The low surface gravity—a hundred pounds on Earth would weigh thirty-eight there—permits a comparable mass of atmosphere to extend two and one half times as far as on the Earth. Were the amount of water and water vapor on Mars increased greatly, the polar caps could never disappear in summer. The greater deposition of snow at the caps could not be melted and vaporized by the solar heat available during the summer period.

The reality and permanency of the markings on Mars can be confirmed by the reader after a careful comparison of the various photographs and drawings in this chapter. The series of photographs in Figure 133 show the planet turned successively about thirty degrees. The ease with which the markings can be followed from image to image demonstrates their reality and is a tribute to the excellent quality of these photographs by E. C. Slipher. A few of the more conspicuous surface features are identified. *Mare* means a sea, *sinus* a bay or a gulf, *lacus* a lake, *lucus* a grove or wood, *fretum* a strait or channel, and *palus* a swamp or marsh. Actually, there are no extended bodies of water on Mars, the names having been given by analogy with terrestrial features. A body of water would reflect the sunlight as a bright point. Notwithstanding careful search, a solar reflection point has never been observed on Mars.

The aquatic names refer to darker areas. The whiter regions in the photographs (excepting the polar caps) are the great deserts. These regions appear pink or orange in the telescope and generally have unqualified names, such as Elysium, Electris, Hellas, etc. The deserts give Mars its red color. The darker areas are green, blue-green or gray in color, with many variations of these shades. Various observers agree rather well in assigning colors to the different regions. Clyde Tombaugh at the Lowell Observatory once sent the author a carefully made drawing of Mars in color. In an accompanying letter he wrote: "It is rare that the observing conditions are good enough (even at Flagstaff) for the colors to come out so beautifully. Three distinct shades of green were noted: (1) the dirty brownish green in the 'Wedge of Casius,' (2) the bright green in the maria towards the south [Cimmerium] and (3) the strong bluish green, more bluish than green, in the Syrtis Major." Other colors appear in the drawing: a "warm coffee color" around the south polar cap, and various gradations of red and pink in the desert areas. The shadings of color were more striking in Tombaugh's drawing than in color reproductions of Lowell's drawings of Mars at the same season, but the general features were the same. Tombaugh wrote further: "One gets these superb views for a few minutes to half an hour out of some forty or more hours of looking at the eyepiece of the telescope."

W. H. Pickering at Harvard carefully studied the colors of the different areas on Mars to eliminate the psychological errors of the eye. Observations of the planet are normally made at night when the eye is accommodated to weak reddish artificial light. Mars, of course, is illuminated by direct sunlight. To compare its color with that of terrestrial substances in daylight, Mars was painted at night with the pigments illuminated by artificial light. The colors were then matched with natural substances in the same light and in daylight. Mars was also observed in the daytime and compared with the same substances faintly lighted by sunlight in a nearly darkened room. After considerable experimenting with various combinations of natural and artificial lighting, Pickering concluded that the desert areas, which comprise most of the planet, are the color "dragon's blood," corresponding to a piece of very red granite, or intermediate in color between an orange-colored brick and a dark red brick. Mars is roughly the color of an average brick. Lowell says that the deserts are reddish ochre. Hence the deserts on Mars are truly deserts in color, similar to the Painted Desert in Arizona.

Pickering concluded also that the apparently green areas are actually green, not dissimilar to arboreal foliage. Schiaparelli, Lowell and other observers of Mars have remarked the striking green and blue-green colorations of certain of the dark areas and the seasonal transformations that they undergo. Lowell's record of color changes in Mare Erythraeum in 1903 is shown in the following table:

Martian date	Aspect	Martian date	Aspect
Dec. 27.......	Blue-green	Feb. 17.......	Faint chocolate
Jan. 16.......	Blue-green	Feb. 19.......	Faint blue-green
Jan. 31.......	Chocolate	Mar. 6.......	Faint blue-green
Feb. 4.......	Chocolate	Mar. 8.......	Faint blue-green
Feb. 13.......	Faint chocolate	Mar. 23......	Pale bluish-green

The maria remained blue-green or green for most of the Martian year but for a short time in the dead of winter changed to a chocolate tone. Lowell and Douglass also reported changes from green to brown, then to yellow.

Antoniadi observed similar color changes around the south polar regions in 1924. He reports, "Not only green areas, but also grayish or blue surfaces, turned to brown, to brown-lilac or to carmine, while other green or bluish regions remained unchanged. The colors were almost exactly those of leaves that fall from trees in summer and autumn in our latitudes . . . But the brown color arrived sometimes early sometimes late in the Martian year and remained for only a short time, proportional to the duration of the brown leaves of our vegetation."*

The darkening of the polar regions with the melting of the cap and the progressive darkening towards the equator were discussed earlier in this chapter. These with their concomitant color changes are overwhelming evidence for the growth and withering of some type of vegetation on the planet Mars. W. W. Coblentz and C. O. Lampland, at the Lowell Observatory, have observed that the noon temperatures of some of the green areas are higher than 86°F., although the twilight temperatures are around 10°F.† The midnight temperatures must be much below zero.

The observers of Mars agree in general with the conclusions so far presented. The questions of the straightness and duplicity of the canals and their interpretation are still controversial. One conclusion is certain; the surface of Mars is covered with detailed markings whose visibility changes with the Martian season and to some extent at the same season from year to year. Lowell and A. E. Douglass maintained that Schiaparelli's *canali* are a geometrical network of dark narrow markings that cover both the dark and bright areas of the disc. Most of the canals were observed to be *straight*—some double—and they generally seemed to meet in *oases*, small dark areas. Because of the artificial character of straight lines, Lowell further suggested that they are waterways, possibly constructed by the Martians to carry their precious water from the melting polar caps to the arable lands of the temperate and equatorial zones. He observed that the canals darkened progressively from the pole to beyond the equator as the polar cap melted.

---

* Translation from "La Planète Mars," p. 18.
† Similar values were observed by Pettit and Nicholson at Mount Wilson.

There is no question that there are dark markings which correspond, at least roughly, with the so-called canals and oases. Practically all of the observers can see these details and photographic plates register the more conspicuous

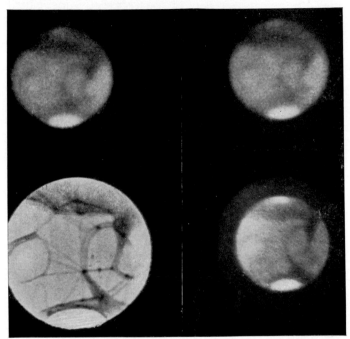

Fig. 134.—Drawing and photographs of Mars.

The upper images are direct photographs of Mars. The lower left is a drawing. The lower right is a photograph of the drawing, at a distance, with the same telescope used for Mars. (*Photographs by E. C. Slipher, Lowell Observatory.*)

ones. A new oasis found at the 1939 opposition is marked in Figure 133. A drawing of Mars is reproduced in Figure 134. To the right of the drawing is its photograph, taken at a distance with the same telescope that registered the two images of Mars at the top of the figure. The close similarity of the photographs of Mars and of the drawing is evident. In original photographs of the planet the general features depicted by good simultaneous drawings are well reproduced. Most of the features in old drawings can be identified in new photographs taken at the corresponding Martian dates.

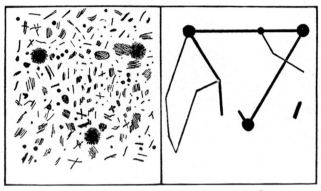

Fig. 135.—Stand several feet from this figure.

Note the similarity of the two diagrams. The canals on Mars may be curves, straight lines, or a succession of smaller markings. (*From W. H. Pickering's "Mars." Courtesy Richard G. Badger.*)

Barnard and, in more recent years, Antoniadi could not see the canals as straight lines nor could they see the narrow double canals. To these observers the surface of Mars, when glimpsed at the rare moments of perfect seeing, was much too complex in structure to be represented by a geometrical pattern of lines. W. H. Pickering and several other observers did not see the canals as straight lines but as generally curved. R. J. Trumpler concludes that a real network of "canals" and oases covers the entire planet, that the "canals" are not straight but gently curved and that a variety of structure and width is manifest. To him the lines are generally diffuse, not fine and uniform. The difficulties of the problem are best illustrated by two drawings made by W. H. Pickering and reproduced in Figure 135. At a distance of several feet, where the eye cannot distinguish fine detail, the two drawings look quite similar. Thus the canals may be chance markings or continuous curves.

That the canals on Mars are actually narrow and straight is considered unlikely by the majority of the observers. The existence of a continuous network of canals is questioned by several.

Thus we find that Schiaparelli's and Lowell's interpretation of the seasonal changes on Mars is now generally accepted, although their arguments for intelligent life on the planet are generally questioned. It is quite possible that some of the canals are old river beds, eroded away when water was abundant. If there is now insufficient water to fill any streams, the atmosphere would transport the water vapor and might well follow the courses of lowest altitude. The exceedingly frigid temperatures at night would remove practically all the water vapor from the atmosphere, and leave a light frost on the ground and perhaps thin clouds of ice crystals. The water that evaporated in the daytime would remain close to the surface as it does on Earth. Thus Lowell's "wave of quickening" would progress down the canals as he observed.* The moisture, however, might be carried entirely by the atmosphere.

There is some uncertain evidence that the green areas are actually lower in altitude than the deserts, although the difference is small, perhaps one to three thousand feet. No great mountains, such as those on the Earth or the Moon, exist on Mars. If the green regions are actually depressed with

---

* Roughly but not minutely confirmed by other observers. Lowell calculated that the water averaged 2.1 miles per hour in its course towards the equator.

respect to the deserts, the general arguments for atmospheric transport of water is strengthened. With so little water and such a thin atmosphere the decrease in temperature and density at an altitude of even a few hundred feet might greatly reduce the water-carrying capacity of the atmosphere, in spite of the small surface gravity and consequent low pressure gradient.

The minor deviations from the normal darkening at corresponding seasons of different years, similar variations in the visibility of the canals and oases, and the general variability in visibility of detailed markings are all suggestive of vagaries in the Martian weather. Where there is so little water the anomalies in precipitation at any point must be tremendous. Figure 136 shows changes in the sizes and forms of various markings on Mars at the 1939 opposition as compared with those at other oppositions. The Solis Lacus region, shown in the three top photographs, is often subject to large fluctuations in appearance. Almost any part of the surface shows variations of one kind or another. There can be little doubt that the vegetation is very dependent upon the meager quantities of moisture from the arid atmosphere.

We might expect the plant life on Mars to resemble desert or high-altitude vegetation on the Earth. Growths would probably be sparse and must be exceedingly resistant to sub-zero temperatures. Desert plants that can survive by storing water for long periods of time might adapt themselves to the rigorous Martian environment. Mosses and shrubbery seem the most likely plant life, as they are the last terrestrial plants to disappear from mountain slopes and arctic tundras.

Although little oxygen and water now remain on Mars, they were probably abundant in the distant past. The red deserts tell the story of the lost oxygen, which may have combined with the iron of the rocks to produce the striking

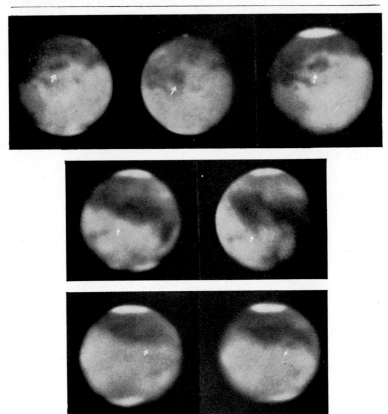

Fig. 136.—Changes on Mars.

Top. Solis Lacus in 1911, 1926, 1939 from left to right. Middle. Changes near Cyclopum Lucus and Sinus Gomer in 1907 (left) and in 1939. Bottom. Changes in Mare Cimmerium 1907 (left) and 1939. (*Photographs by Percival Lowell and E. C. Slipher, Lowell Observatory.*)

shades of red and ochre. The oxygen literally *rusted away.* Lack of mountains suggests that water erosion was also active in the past. The Moon and the Earth have very irregular surfaces, while Mars, intermediate in diameter and mass, presents a much smoother exterior. The small planet, after its formation, probably cooled more quickly than the Earth and, like the Moon, became rigid in an earlier stage of its development. Mountain-forming agencies and isostasy,* both dependent upon internal rock flows, could not alter the levels of the solid surface. Hence erosion had full power to wear away the mountains, flatten the hills and fill in the ocean deeps. Streams and seas, in the remote past, may have rendered Mars as fertile and fruitful as the Earth today.

As the aeons rolled by, the atmosphere thinned and the oxygen and water vapor were lost, mostly by chemical combination with the surface rocks. In addition, the low velocity of escape, only 3.1 miles per second, may have permitted an exceedingly slow but appreciable loss of the atmosphere, particularly of hydrogen and helium. The outermost cold layers of the planet absorbed rather than augmented the supply of gases and liquids on the surface. In such a fashion Mars may have aged, to become the dying world that we observe today.

The great maria and the other dark areas may well be the silt-filled beds of the ancient seas, now the most productive regions of the entire planet. Their lower altitude attracts the infrequent water, whether by intermittent streams or by atmospheric transport, and their soil is fertile. The lack of water has rendered the red deserts barren, like the deserts of the Earth. The Painted Desert of Arizona, an ancient ocean bed stratified by sedimentary rocks, was once a verdant forest region, of which only the petrified forest remains today. The deserts of Mars may well be as beautiful as this incredible area of the Earth—if the winds† of the

---

* See Chapter 6, page 93.

† Terrestrial deserts and mountain tops, however, are often lashed by high winds. Quick and extreme fluctuations in temperature promote windiness.

light atmosphere have been too feeble to fill with sand the gullies and ravines of the ancient watercourses.

Whether intelligent beings exist to appreciate these splendors of the Martian landscape is pure speculation. If we have correctly reconstructed the history of Mars, there is little reason to believe that the life processes may not have followed a course similar to terrestrial evolution. With this assumption, three general possibilities emerge. Intelligent beings may have protected themselves against the excessively slow loss of atmosphere, oxygen and water, by constructing homes and cities* with the physical conditions scientifically controlled. As a second possibility, evolution may have developed a being who can withstand the rigors of the Martian climate. Or the race may have perished.

These possibilities have been sufficiently expanded in the pseudo-scientific literature to make further amplification superfluous. However, there may exist some interesting restrictions to the anatomy and physiology of a Martian. Rarity of the atmosphere, for example, may require a completely altered respiratory system for warm-blooded creatures. If the atmospheric pressure is much below the vapor pressure of water at the body temperature of the individual, the process of breathing with our type of lungs becomes impossible. On Mars the critical pressure for a body temperature of $98°6F.$ occurs when a column of the atmosphere contains one sixth the mass of a similar column on the Earth. For a body temperature of $77°F.$ the critical mass ratio is reduced to about one twelfth, and at $60°F.$ to about one twenty-fourth. These critical values are of the same order as the values estimated for the Martian

---

* Not too large or they might be visible. Perhaps underground, where the atmospheric pressure would be greater and where the temperature extremes would be reduced.

atmosphere. Accordingly the anatomy and physiology of a Martian may be radically different from ours—but this is all conjecture.

We do not know the origin of life, even on the Earth. We are unable to observe any signs of intelligent life on Mars. The reader may form his own opinion. If he believes that the life force is universal and that intelligent beings may have once developed on Mars, he has only to imagine that they persisted for countless generations in a rare atmosphere which is nearly devoid of oxygen and water, and on a planet where the nights are much colder than our arctic winters. The existence of intelligent life on Mars is not impossible but it is completely unproven.

14

ORIGIN AND EVOLUTION

No LONGER CAN THE PHILOSOPHER IN HIS EASY CHAIR expect to solve the basic problems of the origin and evolution of the solar system. A great array of observational facts must be explained by a satisfactory theory, and the theory must be consistent with the principles of dynamics and modern physics. All of the hypotheses so far presented have failed, when physical theory has been properly applied. The modern attack on the problem is less direct than the old method, which depended upon an all-embracing hypothesis. The new method is perhaps slower, but it is much more certain. By a direct study of the facts, we can specify, within an increasingly narrow range, the physical conditions under which the planets evolved. The manner of their origin must finally become apparent.

In the present chapter we will first coordinate some of the more basic observations related to the problem, review briefly the older hypotheses and their more obvious shortcomings, and then follow the first steps along the modern approach to the problem.

It is an interesting commentary on modern science that the *age* of the Earth has been determined, although its origin remains a baffling problem. The oldest rocks in the Earth's crust solidified some two billion years ago. Radioactive substances within the rocks leave minute traces of lead and helium which constitute a measure of the time elapsed since the Earth cooled. Studies of meteorites show that none of these visitors from space have been solid for a much longer period than the crustal rocks. If the meteorites represent fragments of the solar system,* we may conclude that the system is coeval with the Earth. The problem of the origin of the Earth is, therefore, synonymous with the problem of the origin of the entire system. Something happened about three billion years ago to generate the planetary bodies and to produce the order and regularity that we observe today.

Outstanding orderliness is apparent in the planetary motions. The members of the solar system move in the same direction along a common plane. Not only do the planets and a thousand or so asteroids follow this plane in their revolution about the Sun, but the great majority of the satellites move about their primaries in a similar fashion. The Sun, moreover, and all but one of the planets exhibit the same phenomenon in their axial rotation. Even Saturn's rings share in the common motion. We have noted the few exceptions, the Uranus system, Neptune's satellite, a few of the outer satellites of Jupiter and Saturn and notably the comets. Since the comets seem to share so few of the properties of the planets and asteroids, we may well exclude them from our main discussion; cometary evolution appears to constitute a separate and independent problem.

The common motion of so many bodies suggests an initial rotary action, as though the solar system were once sent

---

* Work in progress suggests the meteor orbits are elliptic about the Sun, not hyperbolic.

spinning by some cosmic finger. There is, in fact, so much motion in the outer bounds of the system that the older evolutionary hypotheses have failed in one respect; they cannot explain the *angular momentum* of the major planets. The angular momentum of a planet moving in a circular orbit at a given distance from the Sun* is the product of the mass, distance and speed. Since the speed diminishes only as the square root of the distance, a given mass contributes more angular momentum at a greater distance from the Sun. For a planet moving in an elliptical orbit, Kepler's law of areas† expresses the constancy of the angular momentum at all times. When the planet is near the Sun it moves more rapidly than when it is farther away. No force toward or away from the Sun can change the angular momentum of a planet. Only an external push or drag along the orbit can increase or diminish this fundamental quantity of motion.

Jupiter, with its great mass, carries about six tenths of the entire angular momentum of the solar system. The four giant planets contribute about ninety-eight per cent, and the terrestrial planets a fifth of a per cent. The Sun, with a thousand times the mass of Jupiter, rotates so slowly that its angular momentum is only two per cent of the whole. If all planets could be put into the Sun and could carry with them their present angular momentum, the augmented Sun would rotate in about twelve hours, rather than a month.

A satisfactory hypothesis for the origin of the solar system must first account for the existence of the planets, satellites

---

* Practically at the center of gravity of the solar system.
† Chapter 2, page 24.

and asteroids. It must then explain how they were set moving in the remarkable manner already noted, and must provide the system theoretically with the observed amount of angular momentum. Two types of hypotheses have been suggested. In the first type, the system condensed from a gigantic cloud of glowing gases. In the second, the planets were torn from the Sun by an encounter with a passing

Fig. 137.—Laplace's nebular hypothesis.

The condensation of a rotating gaseous nebula into the Sun, planets and asteroids is here visualized. (*Drawings by Scriven Bolton, F. R. A. S.*)

star. Neither is satisfactory, but both have contributed greatly to astronomy by their impetus to thought.

The hypothesis that was believed for the longest time, excepting the Biblical account, was presented apologetically by the great French mathematician Laplace. According to his Nebular Hypothesis, a rotating and flattened nebula of diffuse material cooled slowly and contracted. In the plane of motion, successive rings of matter were supposed to have split off, to condense into the planets of our present solar system. Most of the matter finally contracted to form the Sun. Between the present orbits of Mars and Jupiter, the ring failed to "jell," and produced many asteroids instead of a planet. The sequence of events is pictured in Figure 137. Figure 138 shows a nebula*—from which the planets could not have condensed.

The Nebular Hypothesis is untenable for several reasons, particularly because a speed of rotation sufficient to leave

Fig. 138.—A spiral nebula
contains more than a billion times the mass of the entire solar system, and, therefore, could not condense in the manner of Figure 137. This one is Messier 33. (*Photograph by the Lick Observatory.*)

nebular rings at the present distances of the planets would provide the nucleus with many times the angular momentum of the rings. The Sun, according to the Hypothesis should have *more* angular momentum than the planets, not one fiftieth as much. Furthermore, James Clerk Maxwell showed that a fluid ring could not coalesce into large planets

* For a detailed discussion of nebulae or galaxies, see "Galaxies," by Harlow Shapley, The Harvard Books on Astronomy.

but would be transformed into a ring of *planetoids*, such as Saturn's ring or the belt of asteroids.

The collision or encounter theories attempt to avoid the difficulties of angular momentum. If another star collided with the sun or passed very close to it, material would be ejected from its surface and might condense to form the planets. Several variations of the encounter theory have been propounded. In the Planetesimal Theory, proposed early this century by T. C. Chamberlin and F. R. Moulton, the passing star was supposed to have raised gigantic tides on the Sun. An appreciable quantity of matter, several times the present masses of the planets, was then ejected from the Sun's surface, and sent spiraling around it by the passing star. Most of the matter was lost or fell back into the Sun, but part remained, with a highly elliptical motion. The gases then condensed into small fragments, the planetesimals, and as time progressed the larger fragments swept up the smaller, to form the planets. The rapid motion of the passing star provided the angular momentum for the orbital motions of the planets, their rotations and the satellite systems. Within twenty million years after the encounter the formation of the planets would have been essentially complete.

Sir James Jeans and Harold Jeffreys have proposed an alternative version of such an encounter. They argue, in their Tidal Theory, that a long tidal filament was drawn out of the Sun by the passing star. The inner part of the filament returned to the Sun while the outer portion escaped into space. A central portion coalesced into a string of beadlike condensations, the embryo planets (see Figure 139).

Jeffreys has more recently abandoned the Tidal Theory as untenable, and has substituted a collisional hypothesis in which the approaching star brushed by the Sun in actual contact. The subsequent phenomena of the filament and planet formation follow essentially the same plan as in the original Tidal Theory. R. A. Lyttleton of Cambridge, England has proposed that the Sun was a double star at the time of the collision. Its companion star was gravitationally torn away by a third star which closely approached the Sun. H. N. Russell had suggested previously that a companion star was struck, and that the planets evolved from its débris.

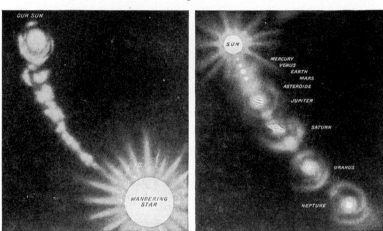

Fig. 139.—The Sun encountered a star

to produce the planetary system. An artist's concept of Sir James Jeans' Tidal Theory. (*Drawings by Scriven Bolton, F. R. A. S.*)

A number of serious objections have been raised against all of these encounter hypotheses. In particular, when mathematical analysis is applied, the observed distribution of angular momentum in the solar system has not yet been explained. A basic objection of another kind has more recently been presented.

Lyman Spitzer, while at the Harvard Observatory, proved by a physical and mathematical demonstration that the planets cannot be formed by a direct condensation of material taken forcibly from the Sun's surface or interior.

Any star such as the Sun consists entirely of superheated gases.* At a depth above which there is sufficient material to form the planets, either by a tidal or collisional process, the temperature is approximately 18,000,000°F. These tremendously hot gases would expand and escape except for the enormous pressure† of the overlying layers, which are forced down by the Sun's great surface gravity. A tidal or collisional ejection, however, would remove the pressure and enable the gases to expand immediately. During a collision, two stars would remain in contact for only an hour or two, and the ejection would occur at velocities of hundreds of miles per second. Spitzer has shown that within a few minutes after their release, the gases would literally explode, long before they could cool by radiation. Even the internal gravitational attraction of a mass twice that of Jupiter would not hold the gases and permit them to condense. Hence planets cannot be formed directly out of matter that is removed catastrophically from the Sun.

We are left, apparently, with some form of the planetesimal hypothesis as the least objectionable explanation for the origin of the planetary system. Spitzer's arguments have not been applied mathematically to the formation of the small planetesimals, but certainly it is true that only a minute fraction of the gases ejected from the Sun would ever be available for forming the planets. Moreover, a stellar collision,‡ rather than an encounter, is required.

There appear to be damning arguments against every theory so far proposed for the origin of the planets. To con-

---

* See Chapter 4, page 51, for a more detailed description of the Sun's constitution.

† At least a million times the pressure of our atmosphere, according to H. N. Russell.

‡ The writer favors the opinion that a stellar collision might produce a gigantic explosion such as is observed in a supernova. An account of

tinue with these involved arguments is beyond the scope of the present chapter. The evolution of the planets, however, can be outlined to some extent from the groundwork of observation discussed in the previous chapters. The correlations of the physical characteristics of the planets are nearly as striking as the uniformity of their motions—and perhaps as significant.

Mercury and the Moon have no atmospheres and are about as dense as ordinary rock; they show little central condensation. Mars is somewhat larger, has some atmosphere, shows a similar central condensation* and is slightly denser, about four times the density of water. The Earth and Venus have thick atmospheres, are considerably denser and show an appreciable central condensation. The giant planets represent the extreme of great atmospheres, low mean densities and high concentration towards their centers. The existence of such a sequence of physical characteristics can be no accident. It must be connected in some manner with the masses of the planets and with their evolution.

The lack of atmosphere on the Moon and Mercury has been explained by their low gravity and consequent small velocities of escape.† But the Earth could hold an atmosphere a hundred times more massive than the present one. Why then do only the giant planets possess their enormous mantles of gas, while the Earth, Mars, and Pluto have relatively thin atmospheres or none at all? This question is fundamental.

---

these tremendously bright temporary stars is given in "The Story of Variable Stars" by Leon Campbell and Luigi Jacchia, Harvard Books on Astronomy.

* From calculations based on its oblateness and rotation.

† See Chapter 9, page 139, for a more detailed explanation of the loss of atmospheric gases.

We must deduce that at some stage in its evolution, a massive planet can acquire more atmospheric material than a less massive one, or that it can hold more of the available gases. A comparison of the compositions of the various atmospheres is enlightening. The Earth and Venus have atmospheres composed of nitrogen, oxygen and carbon with hydrogen combined in water or formaldehyde. Far more oxygen is combined in the crustal rocks of the Earth, however, than in the atmosphere. The giant planets show a much greater abundance of the lighter gases, hydrogen and possibly helium. For some reason these more massive planets have acquired or held the light gases that are relatively rare on the terrestrial planets. It is highly significant that the outer layers of the Sun are composed almost entirely of hydrogen, with considerable helium and a very small percentage of the metals. In addition, the relative abundances of the metals alone are very similar for the Sun and Earth.*

We are now in a position to compare the likelihood of two alternate processes by which the planets may have evolved: (*A*) the planets condensed fairly rapidly from extended masses, and (*B*), they were formed by a slow accretion of matter, planetesimals or otherwise. If the accretion process were sufficiently rapid to maintain a very high temperature at the surface of the growing planet, we could hardly distinguish between processes *A* and *B*, and, indeed, there would be little fundamental difference between them.

According to process *B*, the planetary nuclei were once small. The velocities of escape were also small and the gases

---

* A very complete discussion of the abundances of elements and of theories of origin and evolution in the solar system are contained in H. N. Russell's "The Solar System and its Origin." The author has, to a considerable extent, based the discussion in the present chapter upon the views held by Professor Russell.

could not be retained. After a certain critical mass had been acquired, however, the gases would remain. For oxygen, nitrogen, carbon dioxide and water vapor the critical mass is approximately the mass of Mars; about four tenths the Earth's mass. For helium it is about the mass of the Earth, and for hydrogen nearly the mass of Uranus or Neptune. The values apply for a surface temperature of 2000°F., corresponding to liquid volcanic magma. This particular choice of temperature is of considerable interest because gases dissolved in the magma are released when it cools, and may have provided a considerable fraction of atmospheric gases on the terrestrial planets, regardless of the mode of their origin. Note that the division between retention and loss occurs at a mass approximately that of Mars.

As the nuclear masses of the Earth and Venus continued to grow beyond the present mass of Mars, all of the heavier common gases should have been retained, but most of the hydrogen and helium would have been lost. The Earth as a whole should have retained more than half the available supply of the heavier gases, the great planets practically all of them, plus hydrogen and helium as well. Now we see that we have predicted the observed results. The giant planets possess huge quantities of hydrogen and perhaps helium while these elements are rare on the Earth.* The amount of hydrogen bound up in the oceans and rocks is only a small fraction of one per cent of the Earth's mass.

For nitrogen, however, there is less agreement. H. N. Russell and D. H. Menzel conclude that practically the entire nitrogen supply of the Earth exists in the atmosphere, none being combined in the rocks, and that the element constitutes perhaps only a millionth of the Earth's mass. We

---

* The Earth, apparently, is losing helium. The atmosphere contains less than would have been released by radioactivity.

have already noted, in Chapter 10, that ammonia (three atoms of hydrogen to one of nitrogen) is fairly abundant as free gas in Jupiter's atmosphere, and that far greater quantities are present as crystals in the clouds. Since ammonia freezes and must in great part settle to the bottom of the deep atmosphere, there is little question that nitrogen is moderately abundant in Jupiter. According to an accretion theory of planetary evolution we should expect to find only about twice the percentage of nitrogen on Jupiter than on the Earth. Much more appears to be present. Hence we must view process B with suspicion.

In process A the planets are assumed to have condensed rapidly from extended masses. Whether we consider this process as a very rapid accretion process, as a condensation from a hot gas or even as a condensation from a cold mass of heterogeneous matter, a distinguishing effect follows. The entire mass will be heated to a very high temperature. The contraction of the material towards the center of gravity by the gravitational pressure generates heat. A drop of water or piece of ice falling to the Earth from the distance of the Moon would reach a velocity of about 7 miles per second, corresponding to a temperature of the order of $100,000°F$. The energy released by gravitational contraction must be transferred into heat, whether the fall is rapid or slow.

Thus if the planets condensed rapidly, their surface temperatures must have once reached enormous values. Only the most massive planets could have retained the common gases that we assume were present originally. Hence the terrestrial planets could retain only a remnant of these gases, dissolved in the liquid rocks or magma. These gases escaped as the rocks cooled, and now form the atmospheres of those planets sufficiently massive to retain them. The nitrogen did not dissolve, and so was mostly lost. The giant planets, on the other hand, may have lost a large fraction of the lighter gases but were still able to retain a fair quantity. Our planetary sequence of physical characteristics is somewhat better explained by an evolution process involving fairly rapid condensation than by an accretion or planetesimal hypothesis. The choice between the two processes, however, is not as yet conclusive. The problems are complex.

In spite of the failure of the proposed hypotheses to explain satisfactorily the origin of the planets, the evidence of their physical composition and probable evolution points to an origin in the Sun itself. The similarity of metallic abundances on the Sun and Earth strongly suggests such a conclusion. The overwhelming abundance of hydrogen and probably helium on the Sun accounts for the low density and structure of the giant planets. H. N. Russell has shown that nitrogen (as compared to the metals) is fairly abundant on the Sun and so its occurrence on Jupiter is not surprising. An explanation for its rarity on the Earth has already been mentioned. Oxygen and carbon present no problems.

The Sun, however, is similar in composition to many other stars, so the planets may possibly have originated in the débris from a companion to the Sun or even from a passing star. The difficulty raised by Spitzer, that material forcibly torn from the Sun or a star could not coalesce into the planets, would be invalid were the matter removed slowly. The gases might be permitted to cool by radiation if the overlying pressure were gradually reduced. Some theory of this type or possibly a modified and more rapid accretion process may eventually be developed to satisfy the observations and the theoretical requirements.

So far, our new approach to the problem of origin and evolution has not led to a complete solution. Nevertheless, considerable progress has been made. These conclusions are fairly certain. (1) The planets were once very hot, far above the temperature of melting rock. Even Pluto, now cold enough to hold helium and hydrogen, must have been sufficiently hot to lose the ordinary gases of the Earth's atmosphere. (2) The planets, therefore, grew from a fairly rapid condensation of material, not from a slow accretion process. (3) The planets developed probably from the Sun or possibly from another star. This third conclusion is based largely upon similitudes of chemical composition, but is strengthened by the first two conclusions. Interstellar material, the only alternative to stellar material for planet building, is, within our present knowledge, diffuse. Only an accretion process could produce the planets from diffuse material.

The problem of the possible existence of planets about other stars is still unsolved. If a stellar collision is required to produce planets, there will be only a few systems such as ours among millions of stars. If a single star, unaided, can generate a system of planets, then the number of planets may be enormous.

Returning now from the problem of the origin and evolution of the entire planetary system to the problem of the Moon's evolution, we find that considerable progress has been made. In Chapter 7 we noted that the day and the month are increasing because of the friction of the tides. The length of the day increases by a thousandth of a second in a century and the distance of the Moon by about five feet.

Sir George Darwin* attacked the problem in the reverse sense, to ascertain the history of the Earth-Moon system. He came to the amazing conclusion that the Moon once

---

* Son of Charles Darwin, the naturalist.

revolved at a distance of only 8000 miles from the center of the Earth. The month and day were then almost equal, and only about four hours in length. Darwin then proposed that the Moon had actually been separated from the Earth by the rapid rotation and the disturbances from solar tides. The time was some four billion years ago, consistent, to the accuracy of its determination, with the age of the Earth.

This earthly origin for the Moon is questioned by several investigators, among them Harold Jeffreys, who concludes that although the Moon may have once been so close to the Earth, the tidal and rotational forces were never sufficient to have separated the Moon bodily from the Earth. Nevertheless, it is surprising that two inchoate masses could have originally formed as nearly in contact as Darwin's theory requires. From our point of view there is little choice between the two possibilities. The Earth and Moon were formed practically in contact, or, when the Earth was new, the Moon was born from it. The Moon sprang, possibly, from the region that is now the Pacific Ocean.

We have studied the present state of the solar system, and, to a limited extent, its history. Its future, unless some unforseen accident occurs, seems bright. The chance that a wandering star might disrupt the stately order of the planetary motions is small, even within a billion years. Nor should we expect a great change in the Sun's radiance so soon. Perhaps the Earth is heating slightly because of the radioactivity in its crustal layers. Perhaps the glacial ages will recur; we cannot say. The continents may rise and fall during the ensuing ages, as they have done in the past—we hope they do it slowly. And random meteoric masses may pierce the surface here and there.

But order, which is the solar system, will prevail.

APPENDIX I

BODE'S LAW

THE SO-CALLED BODE'S LAW IS A CONVENIENT RULE FOR recalling the distances of the planets from the Sun. Write down a series of 4's, one for each planet. Add to the successive 4's the numbers 0 for Mercury, 3 for Venus, 6 for the Earth, 12 for Mars, 24 for the asteroids, etc. Insert a decimal point in each sum to divide by ten. The resultant series of numbers represents approximately the distances of the planets from the Sun, in astronomical units. The scheme of numbers follows:

	Mer.	Ven.	E.	Mars	Ast.	Jup.	Sat.	Ur.	Nep.	Pl.
	4	4	4	4	4	4	4	4	.....	4
	0	3	6	12	24	48	96	192	.....	384
Bode's Law..	0.4	0.7	1.0	1.6	2.8	5.2	10.0	19.6	.....	38.8
Actual......	0.39	0.72	1.00	1.52	...	5.20	9.54	19.19	30.07	39.46

Note that Bode's law includes the asteroids and gives the distance for Pluto rather than Neptune. The law was used in Leverrier's and Adams' predictions of the position of Neptune. The predicted orbits were therefore considerably in error.

No theoretical basis for the rule has been found.

247

APPENDIX II

PLANETARY CONFIGURATIONS

THE VARIOUS GEOMETRICAL POSITIONS OF THE PLANETS with respect to the Sun and the Earth are known as the

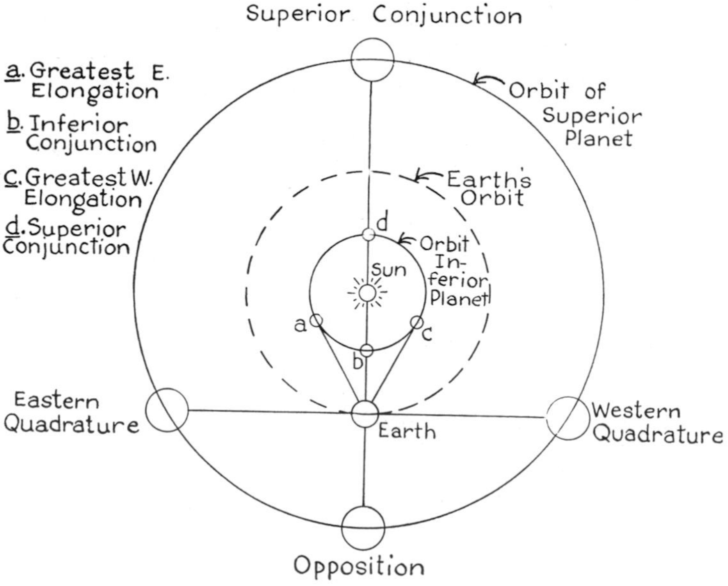

a. Greatest E. Elongation
b. Inferior Conjunction
c. Greatest W. Elongation
d. Superior Conjunction

Superior Conjunction

Orbit of Superior Planet

Earth's Orbit

Orbit Inferior Planet

Sun

Eastern Quadrature

Western Quadrature

Earth

Opposition

Fig. 140.—Planetary configurations.

As seen from the Earth, for an inferior and a superior planet.

planetary configurations. They are shown in Figure 140. For an observer on the Earth the angle between a planet and

248

the Sun is the *elongation*. A *superior* planet, whose orbit lies outside the Earth's, passes through all elongations to 180° East or West. An *inferior* planet, whose orbit lies within the Earth's, may attain only a certain maximum elongation: the *greatest eastern elongation* or *greatest western elongation*. An inferior planet comes to *inferior conjunction* when passing the line between the Earth and the Sun, and to *superior conjunction* when in line with the Sun beyond it.

A superior planet also may come to *superior conjunction* (or simply to *conjunction*). When directly opposite to the Sun, the configuration is *opposition*. The configurations at right angles to the Sun's direction are *eastern* or *western quadrature*.

An inferior planet is best observed near greatest elongation, East or West. A superior planet is best observed at opposition.

APPENDIX III

PLANETARY DATA

TABLE 2

	Mercury	Venus	Earth	Moon*	Mars	Jupiter	Saturn	Uranus	Neptune	Pluto	Sun
(1) Mean Distance from the Sun in Astronomical Units	0.387	0.723	1.000		1.524	5.203	9.539	19.191	30.071	39.46	
(2) Sidereal Period	87d.97	224d.7	365d.256	27d.32	687d.0	11y.86	29y.46	84y.02	164y.8	247y.7	
(3) Synodic Period	115d.88	583d.9	....	29d.53	779d.9	1y.092	1y.035	1y.012	1y.006	1y.004	
(4) Eccentricity of Orbit	0.206	0.007	0.017	0.05	0.093	0.048	0.056	0.047	0.009	0.249	
(5) Inclination of Orbit to Ecliptic	7°.0	3°.4	0°.0	5°.1	1°.9	1°.3	2°.5	0°.8	1°.8	17°.1	
(6) Orbital Velocity, Miles per Second	29.7	21.7	18.5	0.64	15.0	8.1	6.0	4.2	3.4	3.0	
(7) Diameter in Miles	3100	7700	7913	2160	4216	86,700	71,500	32,000	31,000	?	864,400
(8) Volume, Earth = 1.0	0.06	0.92	1.00	0.02	0.15	1312	734	64	60	?	1,300,000
(9) Mass, Earth = 1.0	0.04	0.81	1.00	1/81.56	0.11	317	94.9	14.7	17.2	0.8	332,000
(10) Density, Water = 1.0	3.8	4.86	5.52	3.33	3.96	1.34	0.71	1.27	1.58	?	1.41
(11) Surface Gravity, Earth = 1.0	0.27	0.85	1.00	0.16	0.38	2.64	1.17	0.92	1.12	?	28
(12) Velocity of Escape, Miles per Second	2.2	6.3	7.0	1.5	3.1	37	22	13	14	?	383
(13) Period of Rotation	88d.0	?	1d.0	27d.3	24h.6	9h.9	10h.2	10h.7	15h.8	?	25d
(14) Maximum Surface Temperature Fahrenheit	770°	140°	140°?	212°	86°	−216°	−243°	−300°?	−330°?	−348°?	10,000°
(15) Gases Identified in Atmosphere	None	CO₂	Many	None	H₂O?	CH₄ NH₃	CH₄ NH₃	CH₄ NH₃	CH₄ NH₃	None	Many
(16) Number of Satellites	0	0	1	0	2	11	9	4	1	0	
(17) Albedo	0.07	0.59	0.5?	0.07	0.15	0.44	0.42	0.45?	0.52?	Small	

* *Orbital elements about the Earth.*

250

COMMENTS ON THE DATA OF TABLE 2

Arranged According to the Number of the Line

(1) One astronomical unit is the mean distance from the Earth to the Sun. It is 92,870,000 miles. The mean distance from the Earth to the Moon is 238,857 miles. Maximum 252,710 miles. Minimum 221,463 miles.

(2) The sidereal period is the time of one revolution with respect to the stars. One tropical year (of the seasons) is 365 d. 5 h. 48 m. 46.0 s. It is the unit of lines (2) and (3).

(3) The synodic period is the time of one revolution with respect to the Sun as seen from the Earth.

(4) For definition see Chapter 2, page 23.

(6) and (7) Mean values are given. The Earth's equatorial diameter is 7926.7 miles and its polar diameter is 7900.0 miles. The flattening is one part in 297.

(9) The Earth weighs 6,600,000,000,000,000,000,000 tons.

(11) The weight of a given object on the Earth when multiplied by the quantity in Table 2 becomes the weight of the object at the surface of the planet.

(12) An object shot away from the surface with this velocity would escape forever into space (neglecting friction with an atmosphere).

(13) The Sun's period of rotation varies from $24^{\text{d}}.6$ at its equator to $26^{\text{d}}.6$ at latitude 35°.

(15) CO_2 = carbon dioxide. Formaldehyde, CH_2O, may form the clouds of Venus. See Chapter 12. A table of the composition of the Earth's atmosphere is given in Chapter 6. CH_4 = methane, and NH_3 = ammonia. The clouds of the giant planets may consist largely of ammonia crystals. Hydrogen is probably very abundant in their atmospheres, and probably helium too.

(17) The *albedo* is the ratio of the total amount of light reflected by the planet to the light incident on it.

Miscellaneous

Light travels 186,270 miles per second.

A light-year is a measure of distance between the stars. It equals 5,880,000,000,000 miles.

1 meter $=$ 39.37 inches precisely.

1 kilometer $=$ 0.6214 miles.

1 gram $=$ 0.03527 ounces.

1 kilogram $=$ 2.205 pounds.

(Degrees Fahrenheit) $=$ (Degree Centigrade) $\times$ $\frac{9}{5}$ $+$ 32. 212°F. $=$ 100°C., 32°F. $=$ 0°C.

The data of Appendix III were taken largely from the American Ephemeris and Nautical Almanac and from "Astronomy," by Russell, Dugan and Stewart, Ginn and Co.

APPENDIX IV

THE STAR CHART

THE ACCOMPANYING* STAR CHART IS INTENDED PRIMARILY for use with Table 4 of Appendix 5 to locate and identify the planets at any time from 1940 through 1970. A chart of the north polar region is shown in Figure 46.

The *magnitudes* of stars define their brightness on a reversed scale. A first magnitude star has the average brightness of the twenty brightest stars in the sky. A sixth magnitude star is just one hundredth as bright, and can barely be seen with the naked eye on a very clear dark night. Each magnitude denotes a step of 2.512 times ($\sqrt[5]{100}$) in brightness. Thus a star of the sixth magnitude is 2.512 times as bright as one of the seventh magnitude, and a hundred times as bright as one of the eleventh magnitude, etc.

For the most brilliant stars the values become negative. Sirius, the brightest star in the entire sky, is of magnitude -1.85. Venus, the brightest planet, sometimes reaches a magnitude of -4.3. It is then a hundred times brighter than a first magnitude star. Jupiter, at maximum, reaches a magnitude of -2.5, Mars -2.8, Saturn -0.4 and Mercury -1.2. Uranus is magnitude 5.7, theoretically visible to the

---

* In the back cover of this volume.

253

naked eye, but seen by very few individuals. Neptune is 7.6, easily visible in quite a small telescope, but more difficult to detect.

Venus, Jupiter and Mars are brighter than any star, hence easy to identify in the sky. Saturn is also easily visible, as only a few stars can exceed it in brightness. The planets may sometimes be identified by their steadiness. The stars twinkle much more violently. Mercury is always so near to the Sun that no attempt should be made to find it except at its greatest elongation, and then only under favorable observing conditions.

The constellation identification for groups of stars arose in ancient times, although the names are mostly Latin, Greek and Arabic. In recent years the boundaries of the various constellations have been assigned by international agreement. The brightest star in a constellation is generally called alpha (α), the second beta (β), the third gamma (γ) etc., through the Greek alphabet, although there are many exceptions. (The possessive case is used in such designations.) Many of the stars have proper names as well. The most conspicuous constellations are labeled on the chart and the stars α, β, and γ designated in many of them. The chart is complete to the third magnitude (with only two or three exceptions) and shows a number of the fourth magnitude stars.

The names of some of the brightest stars are given in Table 3 on page 255.

The horizontal line across the middle of the chart is the *Celestial Equator* on the sky. In the United States it can be located when one faces South and looks up at an angle of from 40° to 65° (90° minus the observer's latitude).

The long curved line which crosses the Celestial Equator is the *Celestial Ecliptic*. The planets all appear within about seven degrees of the Ecliptic. The broad band, with the

Ecliptic as its central line, which includes the paths of the planets, is called the *Zodiac*. The numbers along the Ecliptic give, in degrees, the *Celestial Longitude*, corresponding on the sky to ordinary longitude on the Earth. Table 4 gives the

TABLE 3*
The Brightest Stars

Name		Visual magnitude	Distance in light years
α Canis Majoris............	Sirius	$-1^{m}.58$	9
α Carinae.................	Canopus	-0.86	100
α Centauri†..............	....	$+0.06$	4.3
α Lyrae...................	Vega	0.14	27
α Aurigae................	Capella	0.21	42
α Bootis..................	Arcturus	0.24	33
β Orionis.................	Rigel	0.34	540
α Canis Minoris...........	Procyon	0.48	11
α Eridani.................	Achernar	0.60	70
β Centauri................	....	0.86	190
α Aquilae................	Altair	0.89	16
α Orionis.................	Betelgeuse	(0.92)	300
α Crucis..................	....	1.05	220
α Tauri...................	Aldebaran	1.06	53
β Geminorum..............	Pollux	1.21	29
α Virginis................	Spica	1.21	120
α Scorpii.................	Antares	1.22	250
α Piscis Australis...........	Fomalhaut	1.29	23
α Cygni..................	Deneb	1.33	400
α Leonis.................	Regulus	1.34	67
α Geminorum..............	Castor	$+1.58$	47

* *Data compiled by Peter van de Kamp. The light year is defined in Appendix III.*
† *Its fainter companion, Proxima Centauri, is the nearest star.*

celestial longitudes of the planets at convenient intervals of time from 1940 through 1970. The scale along the bottom of the chart is the *Right Ascension* measured in hours of time. 24 hours = 360°; therefore 1 hour = 15°. Right Ascension is like longitude except that it is measured along the Celestial Equator instead of the Celestial Ecliptic.

The vertical scale at sides of the chart is the *Declination*. It is measured North (plus) and South (minus) from the Equator. Declination on the sky is precisely analogous to Latitude on the Earth.

The average plane of the Milky Way, or Galaxy is indicated.

The Star Chart was drawn by Donald A. MacRae.

To Use the Star Chart

Face South with the Chart before You

If the time is 8 P.M. the constellations under the current month will appear in the South. The map will extend over your head and below the horizon.

At 10 P.M. look under the next month, at 12 P.M. the second month etc. At 6 P.M. look under the preceding month, etc.

If you are located in the Southern Hemisphere hold the chart upside down and face North.

APPENDIX V

THE PLANET FINDER

Directions for Its Use Are Given on Page 260

COMMENTS ON THE PLANET FINDER

TABLE 4 GIVES THE POSITIONS OF THE BRIGHTER PLANETS from 1940 through 1970. It was especially calculated for this volume,* and is designed for use with the accompanying Star Chart. The numbers given are the celestial longitudes in degrees. The planets can be located near the ecliptic on the star chart at the corresponding values of the longitude. *Italics* are used for the longitudes of the *morning* sky.

The Sun's longitude is given for the evening of the 13th of each month. The superior planets, Mars, Jupiter and Saturn may be difficult to find when they are near to the Sun on the sky, i.e., near conjunction; the date immediately preceding conjunction is indicated by **boldface.** They can be observed during the entire night when near opposition, indicated by an asterisk.* They are visible in the evening sky for about two months before opposition. Jupiter always lies within 2° of the ecliptic, Saturn 3° and Mars 7°. For Mars this large deviation occurs only when the planet is near

---

* From the tables by Karl Schoch.

258

opposition. See Figure 125, page 209 for the most favorable oppositions. Mercury moves so very rapidly that its longitudes are given at ten-day intervals. When no longitude is given in Table 4, Mercury is hopelessly close to the Sun. Mercury's distance from the Sun at greatest elongation varies enormously because of the eccentricity of its orbit. Each greatest elongation is indicated by at least one value of the longitude. When values of the longitude are given for four consecutive ten-day intervals in Table 4, there is a fair chance, with the naked eye, to identify Mercury on the sky. Choose a night near the middle of the series. When only one or two consecutive values are given there is little chance of finding Mercury without binoculars. When looking for Mercury it is best to estimate the longitude at the date between the values given. Mercury, for the longitudes given, will always lie within 6° of the ecliptic.

The longitudes of Venus are given at fifteen-day intervals. The planet is so bright that it may occasionally be seen very close to the Sun at dates for which the longitude was not calculated, but at such times it will be visible only for a short time in the evening or morning twilight. Venus may lie as much as 7° from the ecliptic.

Venus and Mercury can be seen only in the evening when their longitudes are not in italics. They can be observed in the morning sky only when the longitudes are in italics.

If you lose the accompanying Star Chart and wish to use some other chart, divide the numbers in Table 4 by *fifteen*, to convert them into hours of time. Then use the *Right Ascension* scale of the other chart and locate the planets near the ecliptic as with the present chart.

How to Find the Planets

Locate the year and the month in Table 4. Read the number in the Table for each planet at the nearest date. Locate this number along the curved ecliptic on the Star Chart. Look for the planet near the ecliptic at this point. It is well also to locate the position of the Sun.

If no number is given in Table 4, the planet is too close to the Sun for observation. Do not look for a planet when the number is **boldface, 000,** or immediately follows a **boldface** number. Note the italics *000* for planets in the morning sky. For about two month's before an * in the table, a planet can be seen in the East in the evening.

Venus and Jupiter are brighter than any star. Mars may be a bit fainter than Sirius, the brightest star. Saturn is somewhat fainter but still bright. Mercury is very difficult to find.

See page 257 for the use of the Star Chart.

Read Appendices II, IV and V for more complete descriptions of the Table and Chart and for more details.

Example:

To locate the planets on Christmas Eve, December 24, 1950. On page 266, for December 1950, we find that the table is blank for Mercury on December 23 and for Venus on December 28; the entry for Saturn is in italics. These planets, therefore, are not to be seen. Jupiter, at 332°, is about 10° south of α Aquarii on the Star Chart. The Sun, at 262°, is some 70° away. Jupiter, therefore, is a fine evening object. Mars, at 299°, between Capricornus and Sagittarius, is too close to the Sun and too far south to show for long in the evening.

TABLE 4 1940–1941
The Planet Finder

Planet.......	Sun	Mercury			Venus		Mars	Jupiter	Saturn
Date........	*13th*	*3rd*	*13th*	*23rd*	*13th*	*28th*	*13th*	*13th*	*13th*
1940									
Jan.......	293	...	...	...	324	343	7	3	24
Feb.......	324	...	...	...	2	20	28	9	26
Mar......	353	0	...	...	36	53	47	**15**	29
Apr......	24	*348*	*356*	*9*	70	84	68	*22*	**33**
May......	53	*25*	...	...	95	102	88	*30*	*36*
June......	83	...	105	118	...	...	108	*36*	*40*
July......	111	125	...	...	*87*	*89*	127	*41*	*43*
Aug......	141	...	*123*	...	*98*	*110*	**146**	*45*	*44*
Sept......	171	...	...	...	*125*	*141*	*166*	*45*	*44*
Oct.......	200	211	224	235	*158*	*176*	*186*	*43*	*42*
Nov......	232	...	...	223	*195*	*213*	*206*	*39**	*40**
Dec.......	262	...	...	...	*232*	*250*	*226*	36	38
1941									
Jan.......	294	...	...	...	*270*	...	*246*	36	38
Feb......	325	...	343	...	...	...	*267*	39	38
Mar......	353	...	*329*	*335*	...	...	*286*	44	41
Apr......	24	*348*	*2*	...	...	...	*308*	50	**44**
May......	53	...	...	...	...	...	*328*	**57**	*48*
June......	83	97	104	...	...	...	*348*	*64*	*52*
July......	111	...	...	*101*	134	152	*6*	*71*	*55*
Aug......	141	...	...	...	172	190	*19*	*77*	*58*
Sept......	171	...	191	205	209	226	*23*	*80*	*58*
Oct.......	200	216	222	...	244	261	*16**	*82*	*57*
Nov......	231	...	*212*	...	278	294	11	*80*	*55**
Dec.......	262	...	...	...	307	316	17	*76**	53

000 *Evening.* 000 *Morning.* **000** *Conjunction with Sun.* * *Opposition to Sun.*

TABLE 4 (*Continued*)   1942–1943
THE PLANET FINDER

Planet.......	Sun	Mercury			Venus		Mars	Jupiter	Saturn
Date........	*13th*	*3rd*	*13th*	*23rd*	*13th*	*28th*	*13th*	*13th*	*13th*
1942									
Jan......	293	...	...	322	322	...	31	72	51
Feb......	325	...	...	*312*	...	*306*	48	71	52
Mar.....	353	*316*	*326*	*340*	*312*	*322*	64	73	54
Apr.....	23	...	...	...	*337*	*352*	83	78	57
May.....	52	...	74	84	*9*	*25*	101	84	**60**
June.....	82	...	...	...	*44*	*61*	120	**91**	*64*
July.....	111	*80*	*92*	...	*79*	*97*	139	*98*	*68*
Aug.....	141	...	...	...	*116*	*135*	158	*104*	*71*
Sept.....	170	185	197	205	...	...	**178**	*110*	*72*
Oct......	200	...	...	*192*	...	...	*197*	*114*	*72*
Nov.....	231	...	...	...	...	...	*218*	*115*	*70*
Dec......	262	...	...	...	...	...	*239*	*114*	*68* *
1943									
Jan......	293	...	311	...	...	...	*261*	*111* *	66
Feb.....	325	...	*299*	*309*	346	5	*283*	106	65
Mar.....	353	*320*	...	...	20	39	*304*	105	66
Apr......	23	...	...	52	58	76	*327*	107	69
May.....	52	63	...	...	93	110	*350*	111	**72**
June.....	82	...	*60*	*70*	127	142	*13*	117	*76*
July.....	111	...	...	...	155	165	*34*	**123**	*80*
Aug.....	140	...	164	177	170	...	*54*	*130*	*84*
Sept.....	170	186	...	...	...	*155*	71	*136*	*86*
Oct......	200	...	*182*	...	*159*	*170*	81	*142*	*86*
Nov.....	231	...	...	...	*184*	*200*	80	*146*	*85*
Dec......	261	...	...	*292*	*216*	*234*	70*	*147*	*83* *

000 *Evening.* *000 Morning.* **000** *Conjunction with Sun.* * *Opposition to Sun.*

TABLE 4 *(Continued)*   1944–1945
THE PLANET FINDER

Planet.......	Sun	Mercury			Venus		Mars	Jupiter	Saturn
Date........	*13th*	*3rd*	*13th*	*23rd*	*13th*	*28th*	*13th*	*13th*	*13th*
1944									
Jan.......	293	...	...	*280*	*253*	*271*	65	*146*	80
Feb.......	324	*290*	*302*	...	*291*	*309*	71	142*	79
Mar......	353	...	...	...	*326*	*345*	83	138	80
Apr.......	24	...	43	...	...	...	99	137	82
May......	53	...	...	*39*	...	...	115	138	85
June......	83	*49*	*64*	...	...	...	133	142	**89**
July......	111	...	...	143	...	...	151	148	*93*
Aug......	141	158	168	173	...	...	170	**154**	*96*
Sept......	171	...	...	*163*	192	211	190	*161*	*99*
Oct.......	200	...	...	...	229	248	210	*167*	*100*
Nov......	232	...	...	...	267	285	**232**	*173*	*100*
Dec.......	262	273	...	...	304	321	*253*	*176*	*98**
1945									
Jan.......	294	*263*	*270*	*282*	339	356	*276*	*178*	96
Feb.......	325	...	...	...	11	24	*300*	*176*	94
Mar......	353	...	...	22	32	34	*321*	173*	94
Apr.......	24	...	...	...	...	...	*345*	169	95
May......	53	*18*	*27*	*40*	*18*	*25*	*8*	168	98
June......	83	...	...	...	*38*	*51*	*32*	169	**101**
July......	111	121	136	148	*67*	*83*	*53*	172	*105*
Aug......	141	155	...	...	*101*	*118*	*75*	178	*109*
Sept......	171	*143*	...	...	*137*	*156*	*94*	**184**	*112*
Oct.......	200	...	...	...	*174*	*192*	*108*	*191*	*114*
Nov......	231	...	253	262	...	...	*120*	*197*	*115*
Dec.......	262	...	...	250	...	...	*122*	*202*	*113*

000 *Evening.* 000 *Morning.* **000** *Conjunction with Sun.* * *Opposition to Sun.*

TABLE 4 (*Continued*)   1946–1947
THE PLANET FINDER

Planet.......	Sun	Mercury			Venus		Mars	Jupiter	Saturn
Date........	*13th*	*3rd*	*13th*	*23rd*	*13th*	*28th*	*13th*	*13th*	*13th*
1946									
Jan.......	294	*263*	...	...	...	...	113*	*206*	111*
Feb.......	325	...	...	...	...	...	105	*208*	109
Mar......	353	...	10	...	...	...	106	*206*	108
Apr.......	..24	...	*359*	*6*	...	60	116	*202**	108
May......	53	*18*	*34*	...	78	96	130	199	110
June......	82	...	...	115	115	133	146	198	114
July......	111	127	135	...	150	167	164	199	**117**
Aug......	141	...	...	*133*	185	201	183	202	*121*
Sept......	171	...	...	...	217	229	203	208	*125*
Oct.......	200	...	...	232	239	242	223	**214**	*128*
Nov......	231	241	...	...	...	...	245	*221*	*129*
Dec.......	262	*232*	*242*	...	*228*	*235*	**267**	*227*	*128*
1947									
Jan.......	293	...	...	...	*247*	*262*	*291*	*233*	*126**
Feb.......	325	...	...	352	*278*	*295*	*315*	*236*	124
Mar......	353	...	...	*340*	*310*	*328*	*337*	*238*	122
Apr......	23	*346*	*357*	*12*	*347*	*4*	*2*	*236*	122
May......	52	...	...	...	*23*	*41*	*25*	*233**	123
June......	82	92	106	115	*60*	...	*48*	230	126
July......	111	...	...	...	...	...	*69*	228	**130**
Aug......	140	*112*	...	...	...	...	*59*	229	*134*
Sept......	170	...	...	...	...	...	*110*	233	*137*
Oct.......	200	213	225	231	...	...	*127**	238	*140*
Nov......	231	...	*216*	*221*	...	268	143	**245**	*142*
Dec.......	261	...	...	...	287	305	154	*248*	*142*

000 *Evening.* 000 *Morning.* **000** *Conjunction with Sun.* * *Opposition to Sun.*

TABLE 4 (*Continued*) 1948–1949
THE PLANET FINDER

Planet.......	Sun	Mercury			Venus		Mars	Jupiter	Saturn
Date........	*13th*	*3rd*	*13th*	*23rd*	*13th*	*28th*	*13th*	*13th*	*13th*
1948									
Jan.......	293	...	...	...	325	344	157	*258*	*141*
Feb.......	324	333	...	...	3	21	149	*264*	139*
Mar......	354	*322*	*326*	*336*	37	53	140	*268*	137
Apr......	24	*352*	...	...	70	84	140	*269*	136
May......	53	...	...	85	94	102	148	*268*	136
June......	83	95	...	...	...	...	162	*264**	138
July......	112	...	*91*	...	*85*	*88*	178	261	142
Aug......	141	...	...	...	*97*	*110*	197	259	**145**
Sept......	171	...	195	207	*125*	*142*	217	261	*149*
Oct.......	201	215	...	...	*159*	*176*	238	264	*153*
Nov......	232	*203*	...	...	*195*	*214*	260	270	*155*
Dec.......	262	...	...	...	*232*	*251*	283	**276**	*156*
1949									
Jan.......	294	...	...	320	*271*	...	307	*284*	155
Feb.......	325	...	...	*309*	...	...	332	*290*	153*
Mar......	353	*317*	*330*	...	...	...	**354**	*296*	151
Apr.......	24	...	...	...	...	...	*18*	*300*	149
May......	53	63	74	...	...	...	*40*	*302*	149
June......	83	...	...	*71*	...	116	*63*	*302*	151
July......	111	*81*	...	...	134	153	*84*	*298**	154
Aug......	141	...	...	174	172	190	*105*	294	**157**
Sept......	171	188	197	...	209	226	*124*	293	*161*
Oct.......	200	*190*	*184*	*193*	244	261	*143*	294	*164*
Nov......	231	...	...	...	278	293	*160*	297	*168*
Dec.......	262	...	...	...	306	316	*175*	303	*169*

000 *Evening.* 000 *Morning.* **000** *Conjunction with Sun.* * *Opposition to Sun.*

TABLE 4 (*Continued*) 1950–1951
THE PLANET FINDER

Planet.......	Sun	Mercury			Venus		Mars	Jupiter	Saturn
Date........	13th	3rd	13th	23rd	13th	28th	13th	13th	13th
1950									
Jan.......	294	302	...	...	319	...	*186*	**310**	*169*
Feb.......	325	*290*	*299*	*312*	...	*305*	*190*	*317*	*168*
Mar......	353	...	...	...	*311*	*322*	*185**	*324*	*165**
Apr.......	24	...	...	54	*337*	*353*	174	*330*	163
May......	53	...	...	...	*9*	*26*	172	*334*	163
June......	82	*50*	*59*	...	*44*	*62*	181	*337*	163
July......	111	...	...	...	*80*	*98*	194	*337*	165
Aug......	141	153	167	178	*117*	*135*	212	*334**	169
Sept......	171	183	...	...	...	...	232	330	**172**
Oct.......	200	*171*	...	...	...	...	253	328	*176*
Nov......	231	...	...	...	...	...	276	328	*179*
Dec.......	262	...	282	...	...	...	299	332	*182*
1951									
Jan.......	293	...	*272*	*279*	...	...	323	337	*182*
Feb.......	325	*292*	...	...	346	5	348	**344**	*182*
Mar......	353	...	...	...	21	39	9	*351*	*180**
Apr.......	23	32	...	...	58	76	*33*	*358*	177
May......	52	...	*29*	*37*	93	110	**55**	*5*	176
June......	82	*51*	...	...	127	142	*76*	*10*	176
July......	111	...	130	145	155	164	*97*	*13*	177
Aug......	140	158	165	...	168	...	*117*	*14*	180
Sept......	170	...	*153*	...	...	*153*	*137*	*12*	**184**
Oct.......	200	...	...	...	*158*	*170*	156	*8**	*187*
Nov......	231	...	...	262	*184*	*200*	174	*5*	*191*
Dec......	261	272	...	...	*217*	*234*	191	*5*	*194*

000 *Evening.* 000 *Morning.* **000** *Conjunction with Sun.* * *Opposition to Sun.*

TABLE 4 (*Continued*) 1952–1953
THE PLANET FINDER

Planet	Sun	Mercury			Venus		Mars	Jupiter	Saturn
Date	13th	3rd	13th	23rd	13th	28th	13th	13th	13th
1952									
Jan	293	260	271	...	254	272	207	8	195
Feb	324	...	...	...	291	310	220	13	195
Mar	354	...	...	20	327	345	228	19	193
Apr	24	...	...	10	...	...	226	**26**	191*
May	53	17	29	...	...	...	216*	34	189
June	83	...	...	...	...	...	211	40	188
July	112	125	138	146	...	...	218	46	189
Aug	141	...	...	...	...	...	232	50	191
Sept	171	144	...	...	193	211	251	51	**195**
Oct	201	...	...	...	230	248	271	49	198
Nov	232	244	254	...	268	286	294	45*	202
Dec	262	...	241	252	304	322	317	42	205
1953									
Jan	294	...	...	...	340	356	340	41	207
Feb	325	...	...	...	11	24	5	44	207
Mar	353	1	...	...	30	31	26	48	206
Apr	24	350	358	8	...	...	48	54	204*
May	53	22	...	...	17	25	69	**61**	202
June	83	...	104	117	37	52	**90**	68	201
July	111	126	...	...	67	83	110	75	201
Aug	141	...	122	...	102	119	130	81	203
Sept	171	...	...	...	138	156	150	85	206
Oct	200	...	223	234	174	193	168	86	**209**
Nov	232	222	...	...	...	...	188	85	213
Dec	262	231	...	...	...	...	206	81*	216

000 *Evening.* 000 *Morning.* **000** *Conjunction with Sun.* * *Opposition to Sun.*

TABLE 4 (Continued) 1954–1955
THE PLANET FINDER

Planet	Sun	Mercury			Venus		Mars	Jupiter	Saturn
Date	13th	3rd	13th	23rd	13th	28th	13th	13th	13th
1954									
Jan	294	...	...	...	...	...	*225*	78	*218*
Feb	325	...	343	...	...	...	*242*	76	*219*
Mar	353	...	*332*	*336*	...	...	*257*	78	*219*
Apr	24	*347*	*1*	...	...	60	*270*	82	*217**
May	53	...	...	...	78	97	*278*	88	215
June	82	96	106	...	116	133	*276**	**95**	213
July	111	...	...	*101*	151	168	267	*101*	213
Aug	141	...	...	...	185	201	267	*108*	214
Sept	171	...	...	203	216	228	278	*114*	216
Oct	200	215	224	...	237	240	295	*118*	**220**
Nov	231	...	*212*	...	...	...	316	*120*	*223*
Dec	262	...	...	...	*226*	*234*	337	*119*	*227*
1955									
Jan	293	...	...	...	*247*	*262*	359	*115**	*229*
Feb	325	330	...	...	*279*	*296*	21	123	*231*
Mar	353	*317*	*326*	*338*	*311*	*328*	41	110	*231*
Apr	23	...	...	...	*347*	*5*	56	111	230
May	52	...	73	84	*23*	*42*	82	115	228*
June	82	...	...	...	*61*	...	102	120	226
July	111	*82*	*91*	...	...	...	122	**126**	224
Aug	140	...	...	...	...	...	**141**	*133*	225
Sept	170	184	196	206	...	...	*161*	*140*	227
Oct	200	...	...	*194*	...	...	*180*	*146*	230
Nov	231	...	...	...	...	269	*200*	*150*	**233**
Dec	261	...	...	...	287	306	*220*	*152*	*237*

000 *Evening.* *000 Morning.* **000** *Conjunction with Sun.* * *Opposition to Sun.*

TABLE 4 (*Continued*)   1956–1957
THE PLANET FINDER

Planet.......	Sun	Mercury			Venus		Mars	Jupiter	Saturn
Date........	*13th*	*3rd*	*13th*	*23rd*	*13th*	*28th*	*13th*	*13th*	*13th*
1956									
Jan.......	293	...	*312*	...	326	344	*240*	*150*	*240*
Feb.......	324	...	*299*	*308*	3	21	*260*	*147* *	*242*
Mar......	354	*319*	...	...	37	54	*279*	143	*243*
Apr.......	24	...	...	...	70	83	*299*	142	*242*
May......	53	64	...	...	93	99	*318*	142	*240* *
June......	83	...	*62*	*70*	...	...	*336*	146	238
July......	112	...	...	...	*83*	*86*	*348*	151	236
Aug......	141	...	*163*	177	*97*	*110*	*353*	**158**	236
Sept......	171	188	192	...	*126*	*142*	348*	*164*	238
Oct.......	201	...	*183*	...	*159*	*177*	343	*171*	240
Nov......	232	...	...	...	*196*	*214*	350	*176*	**244**
Dec......	262	...	...	292	*233*	*252*	4	*180*	*247*
1957									
Jan.......	294	...	...	*282*	*272*	...	21	*182*	*250*
Feb.......	325	*290*	*302*	...	...	...	40	*181*	*253*
Mar......	353	...	...	...	...	...	58	*178* *	*254*
Apr.......	24	...	*44*	...	...	...	77	174	*254*
May......	53	...	...	*41*	...	...	96	172	*252*
June......	83	*49*	*62*	...	...	117	115	*173*	*250* *
July......	111	...	...	140	135	153	134	*176*	249
Aug......	141	157	168	175	173	191	154	*181*	247
Sept......	171	...	...	*163*	210	227	**173**	**188**	248
Oct.......	200	...	...	...	244	261	*193*	*194*	250
Nov......	232	...	...	...	279	293	*214*	*201*	**254**
Dec......	262	272	281	...	306	314	*234*	*206*	*257*

000 *Evening.* 000 *Morning.* **000** *Conjunction with Sun.* * *Opposition to Sun.*

TABLE 4 (*Continued*)   1958–1959
THE PLANET FINDER

Planet.......	Sun	Mercury			Venus		Mars	Jupiter	Saturn
Date........	13th	3rd	13th	23rd	13th	28th	13th	13th	13th
1958									
Jan.......	294	266	270	281	317	...	255	210	261
Feb.......	325	...	...	...	...	303	278	212	264
Mar......	353	...	...	...	310	322	298	211	265
Apr.......	24	31	...	...	337	353	320	207*	265
May......	53	20	27	39	10	26	342	204	264
June......	82	...	...	...	45	62	5	202	262*
July......	111	...	135	147	80	98	25	203	260
Aug......	141	157	...	...	118	...	44	206	259
Sept......	171	145	...	...	...	...	58	211	259
Oct.......	200	...	...	...	...	...	63	**217**	261
Nov......	231	...	252	263	...	...	54*	224	264
Dec.......	262	...	...	251	...	...	46	231	**267**
1959									
Jan.......	293	262	...	...	...	...	50	236	271
Feb.......	325	...	...	...	347	6	61	240	274
Mar......	353	...	11	...	22	40	75	242	276
Apr.......	23	...	1	6	59	77	92	241	277
May......	52	17	32	...	94	110	109	238*	276
June......	82	...	...	113	127	142	128	234	275*
July......	111	127	136	...	154	163	146	233	272
Aug......	140	...	...	132	166	...	166	233	271
Sept......	170	...	...	...	...	151	185	237	270
Oct.......	200	...	...	232	158	169	**205**	242	272
Nov......	231	244	250	...	184	200	226	**248**	274
Dec.......	261	...	240	...	217	235	247	255	**277**

000 *Evening.* 000 *Morning.* **000** *Conjunction with Sun.* * *Opposition to Sun.*

TABLE 4 (*Continued*)   1960–1961
THE PLANET FINDER

Planet.......	Sun	Mercury			Venus		Mars	Jupiter	Saturn
Date........	13th	3rd	13th	23rd	13th	28th	13th	13th	13th
1960									
Jan.......	293	...	...	...	254	272	270	262	281
Feb.......	324	...	...	353	292	310	293	268	284
Mar......	354	...	...	342	328	346	315	272	287
Apr......	24	347	357	12	...	...	339	274	288
May......	53	...	...	...	...	...	2	273	288
June......	83	...	107	117	...	...	25	270*	287
July......	112	...	...	...	...	...	47	266	285*
Aug......	141	112	...	...	...	...	68	264	282
Sept......	171	...	...	...	194	212	86	265	282
Oct.......	201	213	225	233	231	249	100	268	282
Nov......	232	...	...	222	268	286	108	274	284
Dec......	262	...	...	...	305	322	105	**280**	**287**
1961									
Jan.......	294	...	...	...	340	356	94*	287	291
Feb.......	325	333	...	...	11	23	90	294	294
Mar......	353	...	327	336	29	...	96	300	297
Apr......	24	350	...	...	...	12	109	305	299
May......	53	...	...	84	15	24	124	307	300
June......	83	96	...	...	37	52	141	307	299
July......	111	...	...	101	67	84	159	304*	297*
Aug......	141	...	...	...	102	120	178	300	294
Sept......	171	...	193	206	138	156	198	298	293
Oct.......	200	216	...	...	175	194	218	298	293
Nov......	232	203	...	...	...	...	240	302	295
Dec......	262	...	...	...	...	...	**262**	307	298

000 *Evening. 000 Morning* **000** *Conjunction with Sun.* * *Opposition to Sun.*

TABLE 4 (*Continued*)   1962–1963
THE PLANET FINDER

Planet.......	Sun	Mercury			Venus		Mars	Jupiter	Saturn
Date........	*13th*	*3rd*	*13th*	*23rd*	*13th*	*28th*	*13th*	*13th*	*13th*
1962									
Jan.......	294	...	...	322	...	...	*286*	**314**	**301**
Feb.......	325	...	...	*310*	...	...	*310*	*321*	*305*
Mar......	353	*316*	*328*	*343*	...	...	*331*	*328*	*308*
Apr......	24	...	...	...	...	61	*356*	*334*	*310*
May......	53	...	*74*	...	79	97	*18*	*339*	*311*
June......	82	...	...	...	116	134	*42*	*342*	*311*
July......	111	*80*	...	...	151	168	*64*	*342*	*309*
Aug......	141	...	...	172	186	201	*85*	*340*	307*
Sept.....	171	187	197	202	216	228	*104*	336*	305
Oct.......	200	...	...	*192*	236	...	*121*	333	304
Nov......	231	...	...	...	...	223	*136*	333	306
Dec.......	262	...	...	...	*225*	*233*	*144*	336	308
1963									
Jan.......	293	302	...	...	*247*	*262*	*142*	342	**311**
Feb.......	325	*292*	*299*	*311*	*279*	*296*	131*	348	*315*
Mar......	353	*322*	...	...	*311*	*329*	125	**355**	*318*
Apr......	23	...	...	53	*348*	6	130	*2*	*321*
May......	52	...	...	...	24	42	140	*9*	*323*
June......	82	*52*	*59*	*72*	62	...	155	*15*	*323*
July......	111	...	...	...	...	...	172	*18*	*322*
Aug......	141	151	166	178	...	...	191	*19*	320*
Sept.....	170	185	...	...	...	...	211	*17*	317
Oct.......	200	*172*	...	...	...	...	232	14*	316
Nov......	231	...	...	...	...	269	254	10	317
Dec.......	262	...	281	...	288	307	277	10	319

000 Evening. 000 Morning. **000** *Conjunction with Sun.* * *Opposition to Sun.*

TABLE 4 (*Continued*) 1964–1965
The Planet Finder

Planet.......	Sun	Mercury			Venus		Mars	Jupiter	Saturn
Date........	13th	3rd	13th	23rd	13th	28th	13th	13th	13th
1964									
Jan.......	293	...	...	*279*	326	345	300	12	322
Feb.......	324	*291*	*305*	...	4	22	**325**	17	**325**
Mar......	354	...	...	...	37	54	*348*	23	*328*
Apr......	24	33	...	...	70	83	*12*	**30**	*332*
May......	53	...	*32*	*38*	93	97	*35*	*38*	*334*
June......	83	*51*	...	...	...	...	*58*	*45*	*335*
July......	112	...	...	145	*81*	*86*	*78*	*50*	*334*
Aug......	141	159	167	...	*97*	*110*	*100*	*55*	*332**
Sept......	171	...	*164*	...	*126*	*142*	*119*	*56*	330
Oct.......	201	...	...	...	*160*	*177*	*137*	*55*	328
Nov......	232	...	...	262	*197*	*215*	*154*	*51**	327
Dec......	262	273	...	...	*234*	*252*	168	47	329
1965									
Jan.......	294	*261*	*272*	...	*272*	...	*177*	46	332
Feb.......	325	...	...	...	...	...	*176*	48	**336**
Mar......	353	...	...	22	...	...	*167**	52	*339*
Apr.......	24	...	...	9	...	...	159	58	*343*
May......	53	*17*	*28*	*43*	...	...	162	**65**	*345*
June......	83	...	...	...	...	118	173	72	*347*
July......	111	124	138	147	136	154	188	79	*347*
Aug......	141	...	...	...	173	191	206	85	*345*
Sept......	171	*143*	...	...	210	228	226	90	*343**
Oct.......	200	...	...	...	245	261	247	*91*	341
Nov......	232	242	254	...	279	293	270	*90*	340
Dec......	262	...	*243*	*251*	306	314	293	*87**	341

000 *Evening.* 000 *Morning.* **000** *Conjunction with Sun.* * *Opposition to Sun.*

TABLE 4 (*Continued*)   1966–1967
THE PLANET FINDER

Planet.......	Sun	Mercury			Venus		Mars	Jupiter	Saturn
Date........	13th	3rd	13th	23rd	13th	28th	13th	13th	13th
1966									
Jan.......	294	...	...	...	...	...	317	83	343
Feb......	325	...	...	...	*299*	*302*	342	81	**346**
Mar......	353	1	...	...	*310*	*322*	4	82	*350*
Apr......	24	*352*	*357*	*6*	*337*	*353*	**27**	86	*354*
May......	53	*20*	...	...	*10*	*27*	*49*	92	*357*
June......	82	...	...	117	*45*	*63*	*71*	**98**	*359*
July......	111	127	132	...	*81*	*99*	*91*	*105*	*359*
Aug......	141	...	*123*	...	*118*	...	*113*	*112*	*358*
Sept......	171	...	...	...	...	...	*132*	*118*	*356**
Oct.......	200	...	221	234	...	...	*151*	*122*	353
Nov......	231	242	...	...	...	...	*169*	*124*	353
Dec......	262	*231*	...	...	...	...	*185*	*124*	353
1967									
Jan.......	293	...	...	...	...	...	*200*	*120**	355
Feb......	325	...	342	...	348	7	*210*	116	358
Mar......	353	...	...	*337*	22	41	*213*	115	**1**
Apr.......	23	*346*	*9*	...	60	77	*205**	116	5
May......	52	...	...	...	94	111	196	119	*8*
June......	82	95	106	112	128	142	197	124	*11*
July......	111	...	...	...	154	162	208	**130**	12
Aug......	141	*112*	...	...	163	...	223	*137*	12
Sept......	170	...	...	202	...	*149*	242	*144*	10
Oct......	200	215	225	...	*157*	*169*	263	*149*	8*
Nov......	231	...	*212*	...	*184*	*201*	286	*154*	6
Dec......	262	...	...	...	*218*	*236*	309	*156*	5

000 *Evening.* *000 Morning.* **000** *Conjunction with Sun.* * *Opposition to Sun.*

TABLE 4 (*Continued*) 1968–1969
THE PLANET FINDER

Planet.......	Sun	Mercury			Venus		Mars	Jupiter	Saturn
Date........	*13th*	*3rd*	*13th*	*23rd*	*13th*	*28th*	*13th*	*13th*	*13th*
1968									
Jan.......	293	...	...	...	*255*	*273*	334	*155*	6
Feb......	324	332	...	...	*292*	*311*	358	*152**	9
Mar......	354	*318*	*326*	*338*	*328*	*346*	20	148	**12**
Apr......	24	...	...	...	...	...	42	146	*16*
May......	53	...	...	86	...	...	64	147	*20*
June......	83	...	...	...	...	...	**85**	150	*23*
July......	112	...	*91*	...	...	...	*105*	155	*25*
Aug......	141	...	...	...	...	...	*125*	**161**	*25*
Sept......	171	183	197	207	194	213	*145*	168	*24*
Oct......	201	211	...	...	231	250	*164*	*174*	*22**
Nov......	232	*204*	...	...	269	287	*183*	*180*	20
Dec.......	262	...	...	...	305	322	*201*	*184*	18
1969									
Jan.......	294	...	313	...	340	356	*218*	*186*	19
Feb.......	325	...	*301*	*309*	11	22	*235*	*185*	21
Mar......	353	*318*	*342*	...	27	...	*247*	*182**	24
Apr.......	24	...	...	...	...	10	*256*	178	**28**
May......	53	64	...	...	*14*	*24*	*255*	176	*31*
June......	83	...	...	70	*37*	*52*	*245**	177	*35*
July......	111	...	...	...	*68*	*84*	242	180	*37*
Aug......	141	...	162	176	*103*	*120*	250	185	*39*
Sept......	171	188	195	...	*139*	*157*	266	**191**	*38*
Oct.......	200	...	*182*	...	*176*	*194*	285	*197*	*36**
Nov......	232	...	...	...	...	...	307	*204*	34
Dec.......	262	...	...	...	...	...	329	*210*	32

000 *Evening.* 000 *Morning.* **000** *Conjunction with Sun.* * *Opposition to Sun.*

TABLE 4 (*Continued*) 1970
THE PLANET FINDER

Planet........	Sun	Mercury			Venus		Mars	Jupiter	Saturn
Date........	*13th*	*3rd*	*13th*	*23rd*	*13th*	*28th*	*13th*	*13th*	*13th*
1970									
Jan.......	294	300	...	*284*	...	...	352	*214*	32
Feb.......	325	*290*	*301*	*315*	...	...	15	*216*	33
Mar......	353	...	...	...	...	...	35	*215*	36
Apr.......	24	...	43	...	43	62	56	*212**	**39**
May......	53	...	...	...	80	98	77	209	*43*
June......	83	*49*	*61*	...	117	134	98	207	*47*
July......	111	...	...	...	152	169	**117**	207	*50*
Aug......	141	156	168	176	186	201	*137*	210	*52*
Sept......	171	...	...	*164*	216	227	*157*	215	*52*
Oct.......	200	...	...	...	234	...	*176*	**221**	*51*
Nov......	231	...	...	...	...	220	196	228	48*
Dec......	262	271	282	...	*223*	*233*	*215*	*234*	46

000 *Evening.* 000 *Morning.* **000** *Conjunction with Sun.* * *Opposition to Sun.*

INDEX